Full of super-fun stuff to keep you busy — turn the page and start reading!
Welcome to your JACQUELINE WILSON Annual 2014
monster from Mars!

THIS BOOK BELONGS TO

Name..

Birthday..

My BFs are

____

____

____

____

____

The thing I like most in this book is

____

____

____

Three of my favourite things in the world

1.

2.

3.

Three things I dislike

1.

2.

3.

All About Jacky

Amaze your friends with your awesome JW knowledge!

NAME: Jacqueline Wilson

BIRTHDAY: December 17th

LIVES: In a Victorian house **full** of books!

Jacky has written nearly 100 books

Jacky's Pinboard

A Favourite Photo

Me with my daughter, Emma.

A List of Great Books

Have you read any of them?

- *Ballet Shoes* by Noel Streatfeild
- *The Family from One End Street* by Eve Garnett
- *Mary Poppins* by P L Travers
- *Little Women* by Louisa M Alcott
- *The Railway Children* by E Nesbit
- *What Katy Did* by Susan Coolidge
- *I Capture the Castle* by Dodie Smith
- *A Little Princess* by Frances Hodgson Burnett

A Person I Admire

Anne Frank

A Childhood Picture

At home with my mum, Biddy, and dad, Harry.

A Place for Inspiration

The V&A Museum — it's full of beautiful things.

A Place I Love

Holkham beach

A Best Friend

On holiday with Nick.

My School Photo

A–Z of JW!

A is for Aitken

My surname before I got married. My mum's name is Biddy and my dad was called Harry.

B is for

Bath, the city where I was born.

Battersea Dogs & Cats Home – I'm an ambassador for this wonderful charity. They do such amazing work for homeless animals.

C is for Cats

My kitties Jacob, Thomas and Lily are so dear to me. I love it when they slink on to my lap for a little cuddle. Jacob and Lily both came from Battersea.

D is for Dolls

I've loved dolls since I was a tiny girl and still do. I have a collection of them, old and new. My dolls often appear in my books. Do you recognise this from *My Sister Jodie*?

E is for Emma

My beautiful daughter. Even though she's grown up now we're the best of friends. We love to visit Paris together.

F is for Friends

I often write about friends in my books. I'm lucky to have lots of lovely friends like Naomi (my publicist), Bob (my driver) and my best friends, Trish and Nick.

G is for Greatest

Who else could this be but Tracy Beaker? She's my most famous character and still incredibly popular. Tracy can be quite naughty, but she's also a very brave and brilliant little girl.

H is for Hetty

My feisty little foundling has grown into a spirited young lady in *Emerald Star*. I very much enjoyed writing the Victorian Hetty stories and she's still one of my favourite characters.

I is for Imagination

A good imagination helps me to write. I've always enjoyed entering an imaginary world and was often told off for daydreaming. Once I was even knocked down because I didn't pay proper attention!

J is for Journalist

My first job was working for a teenage magazine. I got the job after sending in a feature I'd written about discos!

K is for Kingston upon Thames

We moved from Bath to Kingston when I was just over a year old and stayed with my Ga and Gongon. I still live there now.

L is for Lola Rose

Jayni has to change her name to hide from danger. To keep her identity a secret, Nick originally didn't draw her picture. But now he's created a brand new cover for the book and you can see her for the first time!

M is for Maggots

When I was nine I wrote my first novel, *Meet The Maggots*. It wasn't very long and it wasn't published. I drew little illustrations for the story and I've kept the tattered notebook safe to this day.

N is for Nick

Nick's illustrations really bring my characters to life. My books wouldn't be the same without them. He's one of my best friends too!

O is for Old-fashioned

I'm not great with gadgets and am very traditional when it comes to writing. I write every story in longhand before I start typing. You can see some of my notebooks on page 26.

P is for Presents

I'm very lucky to have received some very special gifts. I've had all sorts of beautiful things made for me by readers, hand-made jewellery, gorgeous shoes and even an *Emerald Star* doll!

Q is for

Queen – My favourite rock band.

The Queen – I've met her a few times.

Queenie – My first book release in 2013.

R is for Reading

I'm always reading something. Books, letters, newspapers — you name it, I'm reading it! I have over 20,000 books in my house!

S is for School

I didn't always do well at school — and certainly not at sport or maths! My best subjects were English and art.

T is for Treasures

I love to wear my bold silver jewellery. I have a big collection now and one of my favourite pieces is this beautiful blue moonstone necklace.

U is for Undies

Tracy Beaker put hers on the top of a tree!

V is for Victorians

I love things from the Victorian era — my house is Victorian and I have lots of interesting ornaments and knick-knacks from that era. But I'm glad I live in a modern age — I wouldn't want to be a servant like Hetty!

W is for Wedding

This is me on my wedding day — I was only 19! I was married to Millar for a long time but we're not married now.

X is for X Factor

I enjoy watching shows like *The X Factor*, *Strictly Come Dancing* and *Britain's Got Talent*. It's the perfect way to relax.

Y is for Young

I was only 17 when I moved from the south of England all the way to Scotland for my first job. I stayed in a tiny linen cupboard in a hostel for Young Ladies.

Z is for Zodiac

I used to edit the horoscope column on the magazine I worked for. I eagerly read my lucky stars each week and hoped they would come true. I think they have, don't you?

A Day in the Life of JW

What's it like to be a best-selling author? Jacky tells us!

Each morning I relax on my pink velvet chaise longue and write for a few hours. Jacob often cuddles up beside me and peers out of the window. Lily might join in too because she loves to be next to her big brother!

I write all my books by hand in pretty notebooks — my favourite ones have beautiful marbled paper covers like this. When I've finally finished I type up the whole story on my computer, making any changes as I go.

No two days are the same and they're usually very busy. I may have meetings with my agent or publisher to make plans for my books, or have a radio or TV interview.

Sometimes I do events like talks at book festivals. Nick might join me, doing some of his wonderful sketches.

On a book tour there's a lot of travelling. Luckily I'm accompanied by my dear friends Naomi (my publicist) and Bob (my driver). Sometimes my best friend comes along too.

It's super to meet my readers in person — I get so many ideas from chatting to you all!

If I'm not having a busy day, I enjoy going for a walk. I often get inspired when I'm walking — the idea for *Lily Alone* popped into my head as I strolled around the park.

At night I like to watch a little TV and catch up on all the lovely letters and emails you send me. I especially like it when Jacob, Thomas and Lily cuddle up together nearby.

But sometimes I have a glamorous evening out to an event or party. To celebrate a book launch my publishers once held a very fancy party for me at the Ritz Hotel. I love to get dressed up in a gorgeous outfit, sparkly high heels and lots of jewellery!

Find Your JW

START
TRACY BEAKER IS MY FAVOURITE TV SHOW.
YES
NO
MY MUM IS MY BF.
YES
NO
I ALWAYS WEAR A NECKLACE.
YES
NO
I'M GOING ABROAD FOR THE HOLIDAYS.
YES
NO
I WOULD CUT MY LONG HAIR.
YES
NO
I'VE READ JACKY'S LATEST BOOK.
YES
NO
I LOVE ICE CREAM.
NO
YES
I'M REALLY GOOD AT ART.
NO
YES
I'M AN ONLY CHILD.
YES

Style!

Did You Know?
Jacky loves wearing bold black or shimmering silver nail polish too!

Silver Ring

You think **Jacky**'s chunky rings are amazing and would love to try them on. Copy her style by wearing a ring on every finger or why not try designing a special JW-style ring for yourself?

I HAVE A LOVELY JEWELLERY BOX.

NO / YES

I SPEND LOTS IN CLAIRE'S ACCESSORIES.

YES / NO

I LIKE LITTLE MIX.

NO / YES

I LIKE PAINTING MY NAILS.

YES / NO

I'M GOOD AT TELLING JOKES.

YES / NO

I USUALLY TIE MY HAIR BACK.

YES / NO

SWIMMING IS MY TOP SPORT.

YES / NO

Cool Cropped Hair

You love **Jacky**'s funky short style, but are you brave enough to wear it yourself? If not, you can bling up your style with glittering clips and hot hairbands.

Chunky Necklace

Jacky's show-stopping lockets and stone necklaces are so you. **Jacky** wears them to perfectly set off her black and grey outfits, so match a chunky chain with a plain top for a sassy new style!

What's Your Author Name?

In *Midnight*, the rather plain Colin Dunwell transforms himself into mystical Casper Dream. Create *your* amazing name here...

FIRST NAME

Write down your date of birth. Now add all the numbers together. Keep adding till you get 9 or less.

For example –

Your birthday: 17.12.99

1 + 7 + 1 + 2 + 9 + 9 = 29

2 + 9 = 11

1 + 1 = 2

1. Dollie
2. Carolina
3. Precious
4. Venitia
5. Mazarine
6. Cherry
7. Bronte
8. Iolanthe
9. Ekaterina

LAST NAME

Match the first letter of your own last name to get your fabulous surname.

A — Azuline
B — Butterberry
C — Clitheroe
D — Dillydally
E — Elfinshoe
F — Followfox
G — Glimmershimmer
H — Hippityhop
I — Inkwell
J — Jesaray
K — Kandydrop
L — Lollapalooza
M — Mallowfeather
N — Nightingale
O — Oleander
P — Poppinpetal
Q — Quartzglo
R — Rainsparkle
S — Silverspirit
T — Treetops
U — Umbrella
V — Vanillablossom
W — Woollysocks
X — Xavier
Y — Yolande
Z — Zebrastripes

Practise writing your superstar signature here...

Did You Know?

Jacky's author name is Carolina Woollysocks

How to be an amazing author — just like ~~Jacky~~ me!!
JW
STORY SCHOOL
JW
All the tips and writing secrets you'll ever need!
Jacqueline Wilson
Children's Laureate 2005-2007
Illustrated by Nick Sharratt
Jacqueline Wilson
The worst thing about my sister
Can tomboy Marty and girlie Melissa ever get along?
Illustrated by Nick Sharratt
Jacqueline Wilson
Bad Girls
Jacqueline Wilson
Best Friends
Illustrated by Nick Sharratt
Jacqueline Wilson
The Story of Tracy Beaker

Setting the Scene!

We show you how to describe a scene — it's all about the detail!

Where is your story set? Is it in the past, the present, or the future? Hetty Feather is set in the past, but the Tracy Beaker books are in the present.

Get started by ticking the colour you're most drawn to —

Past ☐ Present ☐ Future ☐

Where is your character? Are they inside or outside? Are they in the middle of a city, with loads people pushing past them and traffic honking in the background, or are they in a quiet cottage in the middle or nowhere?

Tick the colour you're most drawn to —

- Inside a quiet cottage ☐
- In the middle of a busy street ☐
- Alone, in the forest ☐

What are the surroundings like? If they're inside a house, is the room super posh with plumped-up cushions and expensive ornaments? Or is it shabby, with threadbare carpets and moth-eaten curtains? Think carefully and describe it for your reader here ...

....

....

....

....

....

What time is it? Is it the middle of the day or night time? Are there rays of moonlight shining through the window and dogs howling in the background or is it a lovely sunny day with birds tweeting merrily and children playing nearby?

Tick the colour you're most drawn to —

- Daytime ☐
- Dusk ☐
- The middle of the night ☐

Think about your characters' senses. Can they see, hear or smell anything — and does it remind them of something else? It could be anything from a wafting scent of cheeseburger to a shout for help that jolts them awake!

Tick the colour you're most drawn to —

- They hear something ☐
- They smell something ☐
- They see something ☐

Now use the choices you made to set your scene. Happy writing!

Guess The Book!

Can you match the correct book title to these scene descriptions?

1 Men dressed up as eggs, bacon, cups of tea and packets of cornflakes were also parading along, having to take mincing little steps because of their big polystyrene costumes.

2 But there's still a sofa in the living room, quite a swish one, red velvet. Some plonker's put his muddy boots all over it, but I've been scratching at it with my fingernails and I think it'll clean up a treat.

3 We trudged back along the pizza-smelling corridors in our shabby trainers, wishing we could stay in Glassworld for ever.

4 I saw their coarse dark coats, their long snouts, their great teeth — and I thought of grandmothers and little girls in red hooded cloaks.

- *Clean Break* ☐
- *Kiss* ☐
- *Hetty Feather* ☐
- *The Dare Game* ☐

Answers:
1) *Clean Break*
2) *The Dare Game*
3) *Kiss*
4) *Hetty Feather*

Easy Peasy Story Starter

Starting a story is sometimes the most difficult part of writing...

WHAT TO DO:

Roll a dice to pick a choice from each section. When you've picked them all, you've got a few ideas to start your amazing story! Now you just need to figure out what happens next...

You can play over and over again to get lots of different stories.

My main character is...

1) Mischievous
2) Super quiet
3) A troublemaker
4) Caring
5) Cheeky
6) Shallow and vain

They live...

1) In a huge mansion
2) All alone
3) With their best friend
4) In a foster home
5) In a camper van
6) In a spooky cottage

They woke up feeling...

1) Fabulous
2) Grumpy
3) Super–tired
4) Scared
5) Full of regret
6) Lonely

They felt this way because

1) They'd accidentally spilled a secret
2) They'd fallen out with their bestie
3) They had no money
4) Their dreams had all come true
5) They couldn't remember what had happened yesterday
6) Everything had gone wrong!

They decide that they're going to...

1) Apologise!
2) Order a pepperoni pizza
3) Call their bestie
4) Run away from home
5) Track down the culprit
6) Throw a tantrum immediately

What happens next? You decide!

Opening Sentences

Jacky is great at starting her stories. Match these books to their opening sentences —

1) 'I've got a surprise for you girls,' said Mum.

....

2) Jodie. It was the first word I ever said.

....

3) When my parents split up they didn't know what to do with me.

....

4) Have you ever wondered what you'd do if you won the lottery?

....

5) I had two birthdays in one week.

....

Answers:
1) The Diamond Girls
2) My Sister Jodie
3) The Suitcase Kid
4) Lola Rose
5) Candyfloss

How to Write a Happy Ending

Top tips for ending your story on a happy note!

Jacky's book *Double Act* has an interesting happy ending even though the story itself has plenty of ups and downs. Although Ruby and Garnet are living apart and missing each other lots, the book ends with them realising how much they mean to one another.

Setting the Scene...

It's important to really set the scene for a happy ending — take your time adding lots of detail, rather than rushing to finish your story. Think about:

- Where the happy ending takes place. Maybe it's in a fancy house, or a beautiful park?

- Who else is there? Is the main character alone, or with a special friend or family member?
- The main character's emotions. How are they feeling before the ending — sad, anxious, excited?
- Adding lots of descriptive words think about sounds, smells, colours and textures!

The Happy Ending Game

Try to create a happy ending for these sad stories. Cut out the spinner on page 89 to get started. Play with friends, where you only have 30 seconds to come up with a happy ending or you get knocked out! Or play alone and give yourself more time to write down your ideas.

1. A young girl has been bullied at school for years. One day as she's walking home, she comes face-to-face with her biggest bully in a deserted alleyway. Things aren't looking good...

2 A family's treasured pet cat is hit by a car at night. The driver speeds off into the distance, leaving the cat on the road. It cries out for help, but nobody hears it...

3 Two best friends have an awful argument and end up not speaking to each other for weeks. Then one of them finds out she's moving to Australia with her family. Will they ever see each other again?

4 A lonely old man sits alone in his cold house. Surely there must be more to life than this, he wonders. Little does he know, things are about to change in a big way...

5 A shopkeeper is devastated when her beautiful clothes store burns down in a terrible fire. How will she make a living now? She doesn't have much money and feels helpless...

6 A little boy loses his favourite toy while at the zoo. His mother promises to buy him another one, but he knows it won't be the same. What will he do without it?

Why not create names for these characters and develop the stories further to make them longer?

What's Your Perfect Ending?

Pick one choice for each question to reveal your own ideal ending...

1. Your perfect weekend would be spent...

a) Going camping somewhere you haven't been before
b) Practising your singing, dancing or acting
c) Reading as many books as possible

2. The word which best describes you is...

a) Adventurous
c) Creative
b) Outgoing

3. Your favourite animal is...

b) A dog
c) A cat
a) A dolphin

4. Your favourite lesson at school is...

c) English
a) Geography
b) Drama

5. You're doing a talk at school, what's the subject?

c) Your favourite book or author
b) Your favourite film or TV show
a) The best holiday you've ever had

You chose...

Mostly As:
Your happy ending would be moving abroad to an exotic location!

Mostly Bs:
Your happy ending would be becoming a super-famous celebrity!

Mostly Cs:
Your happy ending would be to have your own book published!

Not a fan of happy ever after? Turn the page for drama...

Create A Cliffhanger!

Write an exciting end to your story!

If happily-ever-after endings just aren't your style, then why not finish your story on a cliffhanger? This means ending your tale with a dramatic scene which leaves readers wondering what happens next.

Jacky's book, *Clean Break*, ends on a cliffhanger. Em and her family are tucked up in bed on Christmas Eve when suddenly there's a frantic knock on the door. Who could it be? Jacky doesn't say and so the ending is left to your imagination. Chapters can end on cliffhangers, too — this keeps the reader turning pages. Jacky puts lots of exciting parts into her stories so that you just can't wait to read on.
Can you guess which books these cliffhangers come from?

1

And now I'm stuck in the Quiet Room and it's gone twelve and one of the other kids will get to go out to lunch with Cam instead of me and I don't care. At least it won't be Justine. Maybe my mum will come.
There's someone outside the door. It's opening!
Is it Mum???

2

'No, go back to the set!' said Harley, stumbling to his feet. I jumped up too and we started running.
The garden tractor roared — and then there was a high-pitched scream.

3

I sat watching the minute hand tick round and round, and I could feel my heart inside my chest going *tick, tick, tick* too. It was eight o'clock now. Nan was always home by this time

4

'The baby's fine,' says Jack. 'A little boy, six and a half pounds.' He reaches out and takes my hand. He's horribly hot and clammy. I can't say a word. I want to run away. I know there's something terribly wrong.

5

'There's your duffle bag! Is that where the awful smell is coming from? Don't say you've left your wet swimming things in there all this time?'
She seized the duffle bag, pulled it out into the open, undid the top... and tipped the contents onto the carpet.

Top Tips!

- Cliffhangers don't have to just be scary. They might be super-exciting, sad or funny!
- Try creating a cliffhanger and then writing two different endings to it.
- Write an extra chapter for your favourite JW book, but finish it on a cliffhanger!

Why not try writing your own cliffhanger end to a story? Make sure it leaves the reader desperate to find out what happens next!

Stuck for ideas?

Use the Destiny Decider to help you choose a dramatic cliffhanger for your story!

What to do:

- Cut out the Destiny Decider from page 91 and follow the folding instructions to make it.
- Pick a word from one of the four corners.
- Count the letters in the word and open and close the Destiny Decider the same number of times.
- Now pick a number and open and close as you count out the numbers.
- Choose a final number and lift the flap to find your spectacular cliffhanger!

Answers 1. The Story of Tracy Beaker 2. My Sister Jodie 3. Queenie 4. The Longest Whale Song 5. The Cat Mummy

Not Perfect? No Problem!

No one can sit down and write the perfect story first time — not even Jacky!

Did you know that when Jacqueline starts to write a new story, she doesn't sit down at a computer or typewriter? Instead, Jacky prefers to write her stories by hand into beautiful notebooks like this

Sneak a peek at some of Jacky's handwritten pages!

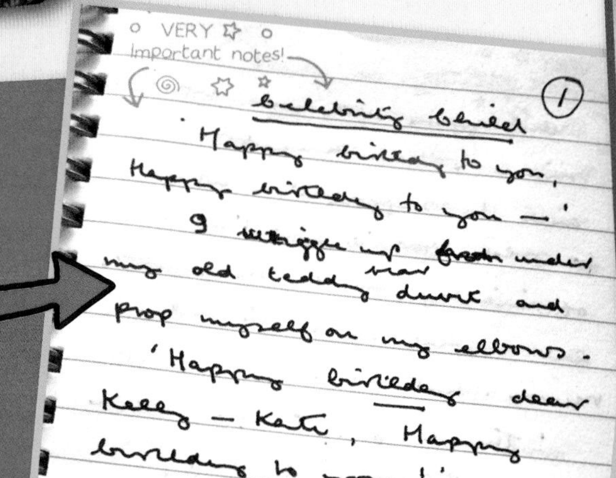

1

Celebrity Child

'Happy birthday to you,
Happy birthday to you—'
I wriggle up from under
my old teddy bear duvet and
prop myself on my elbows.
'Happy birthday dear
Kelly—Kate, Happy
birthday to you!'
Mum tucks [illegible] the duvet, trying to make
the two big bears mouths
like puppets, doing
growly bear Happy
Birthdays. She's pleased

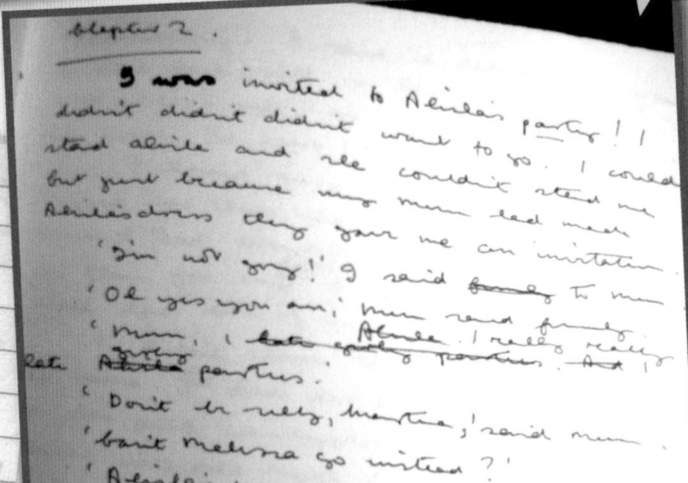

Chapter 2.

I was invited to Alicia's party! I didn't didn't didn't want to go. I couldn't stand Alicia and she couldn't stand me but just because my mum had made Alicia's dress they gave me an invitation.
'I'm not going!' I said to mum.
'Oh yes you are,' mum said firmly.
'Mum, I really really hate going to parties.'
'Don't be silly, Martina,' said mum.
'Can't Melissa go instead?'
'Alicia's your friend, silly.'
'No she's not. She's just in my class at school. And I hate her.'
'You don't hate her, you just don't like her very much,' said mum.
'Exactly, so why should I have to go to her party if I don't like her very much,' I said.
'Because — because I don't want to offend Mrs Evans,' said mum.
'Why aren't you worried about offending me?' I said, stamping off to my room.

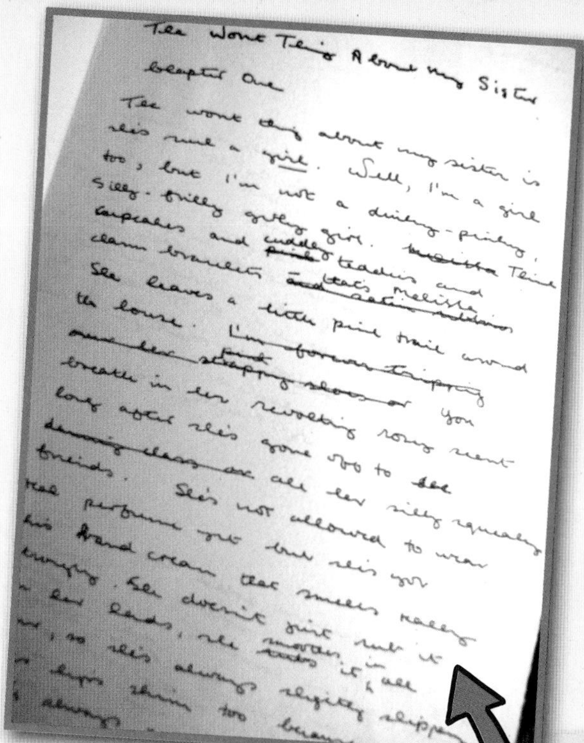
The Worst Thing About My Sister

Chapter One

The worst thing about my sister is she's such a girl. Well, I'm a girl too, but I'm not a dinky-pinky silly-frilly girly girl.

This is the first chapter of *The Worst Thing About My Sister*. If you read the first page of the finished book you might spot a few things that are different from this handwritten original.

Jacky will often go back, read through her stories and then make changes. Look closely and you'll see where Jacky has scored out some words and replaced them.

Every writer does this, so once you've finished your story, read it over and rewrite or swap bits around to make it even better!

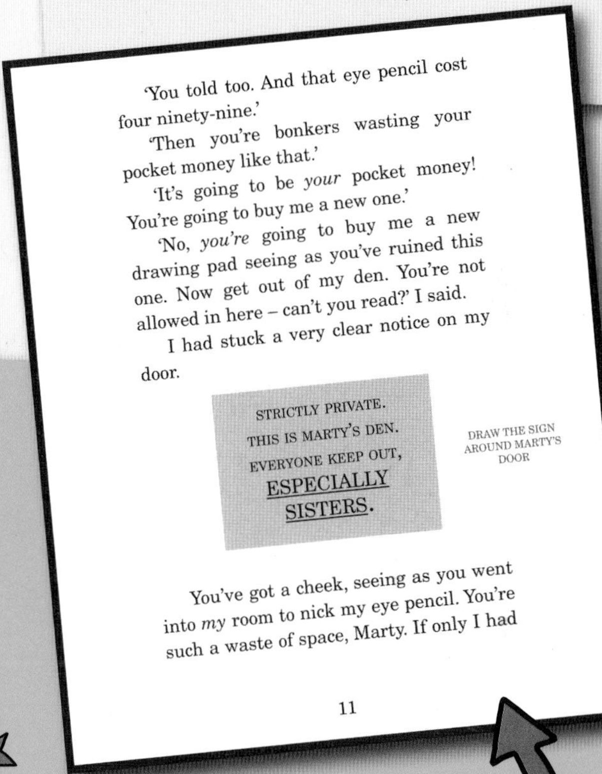
'You told too. And that eye pencil cost four ninety-nine.'

'Then you're bonkers wasting your pocket money like that.'

'It's going to be *your* pocket money! You're going to buy me a new one.'

'No, *you're* going to buy me a new drawing pad seeing as you've ruined this one. Now get out of my den. You're not allowed in here – can't you read?' I said.

I had stuck a very clear notice on my door.

STRICTLY PRIVATE.
THIS IS MARTY'S DEN.
EVERYONE KEEP OUT,
ESPECIALLY SISTERS.

DRAW THE SIGN AROUND MARTY'S DOOR

You've got a cheek, seeing as you went into *my* room to nick my eye pencil. You're such a waste of space, Marty. If only I had

11

Before the book goes to press, one of the most special ingredients has to be added in — Nick Sharratt's amazing artwork! here you can see exactly what Jacky would like Nick to add do for each page. When Nick has finished his illustrations they will be slotted into the correct places and the book is finally ready to print.

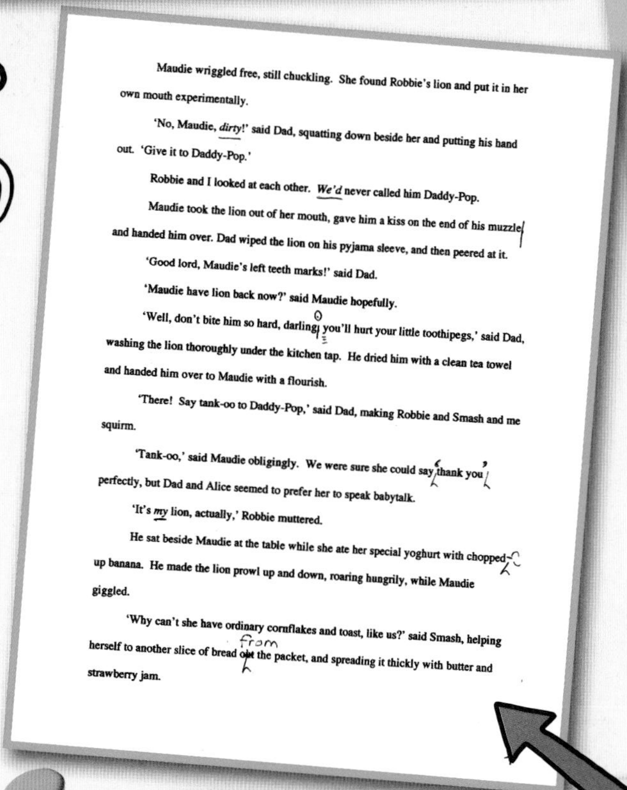
Maudie wriggled free, still chuckling. She found Robbie's lion and put it in her own mouth experimentally.

'No, Maudie, *dirty*!' said Dad, squatting down beside her and putting his hand out. 'Give it to Daddy-Pop.'

Robbie and I looked at each other. *We'd* never called him Daddy-Pop.

Maudie took the lion out of her mouth, gave him a kiss on the end of his muzzle and handed him over. Dad wiped the lion on his pyjama sleeve, and then peered at it.

'Good lord, Maudie's left teeth marks!' said Dad.

'Maudie have lion back now?' said Maudie hopefully.

'Well, don't bite him so hard, darling, you'll hurt your little toothipegs,' said Dad, washing the lion thoroughly under the kitchen tap. He dried him with a clean tea towel and handed him over to Maudie with a flourish.

'There! Say tank-oo to Daddy-Pop,' said Dad, making Robbie and Smash and me squirm.

'Tank-oo,' said Maudie obligingly. We were sure she could say 'thank you' perfectly, but Dad and Alice seemed to prefer her to speak babytalk.

'It's *my* lion, actually,' Robbie muttered.

He sat beside Maudie at the table while she ate her special yoghurt with chopped-up banana. He made the lion prowl up and down, roaring hungrily, while Maudie giggled.

'Why can't she have ordinary cornflakes and toast, like us?' said Smash, helping herself to another slice of bread ~~out~~ from the packet, and spreading it thickly with butter and strawberry jam.

When Jacqueline is finally happy the book is sent to her publisher. There, an editor will read it and often suggest even more changes. These are marked on the page like this and then the script is altered again. This process can happen a few times before the story is 100% finished!

You can see a story goes through a lot of changes before it appears as a book. So don't fret, just keep calm and carry on writing. Focus on being as creative as you can with your stories — you can fix any little mistakes when you're finished!

Rejection - Can You Handle It?

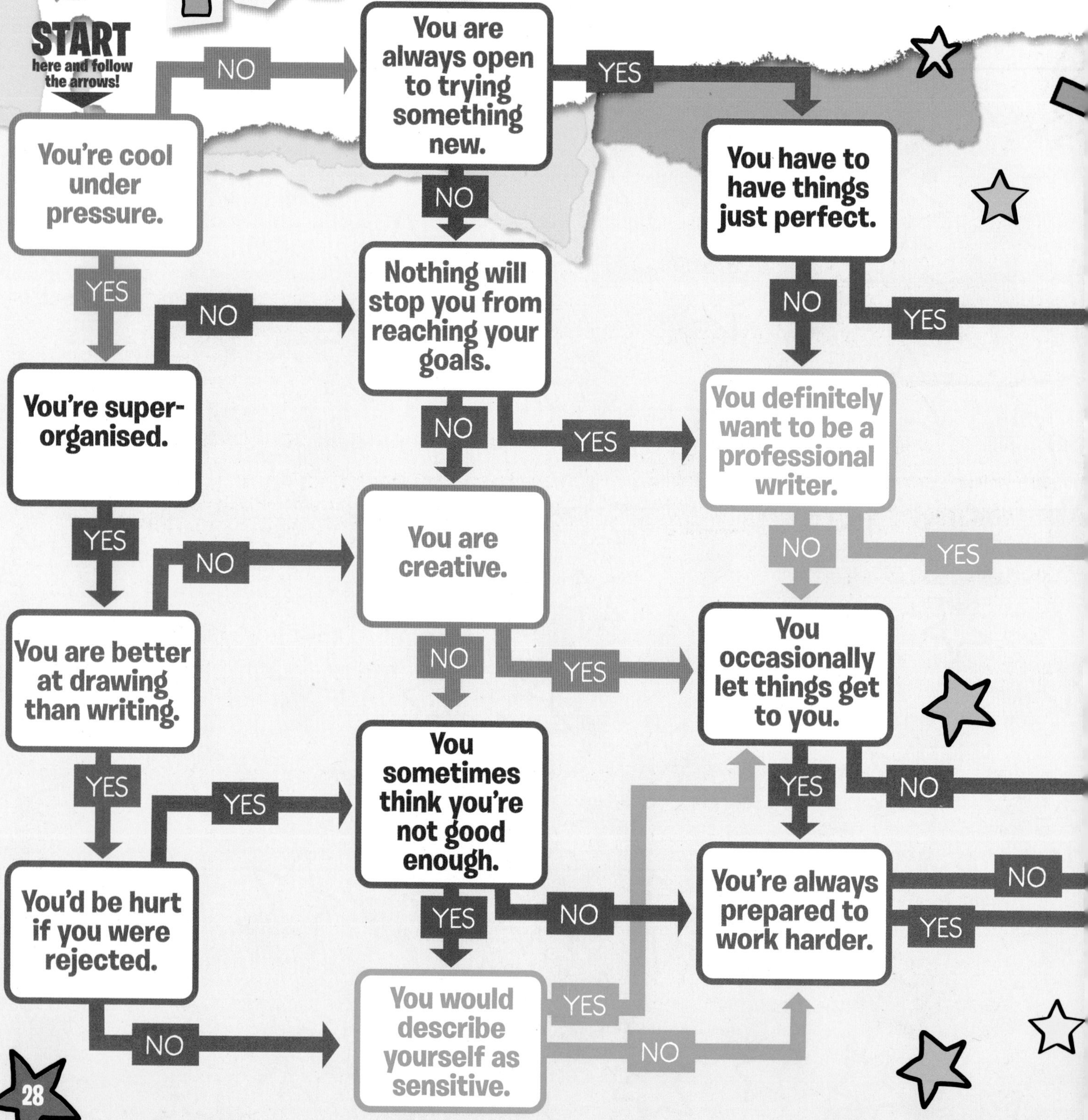

You'd love to be a top author like Jacky but writers can hear a lot of 'no's before they get a 'yes'. Have you got what it takes to keep going?

You never take 'no' for an answer!
YES → Totally Tracy!
NO → Destined To Be A Star

You never accept second best.
YES → Totally Tracy!
NO → Brilliant Like Beauty

You wish you were braver.
NO → Destined To Be A Star
YES → Brilliant Like Beauty

Totally Tracy!

Tracy is disappointed every time her mum fails to visit, but she still believes 100% that Beaker is the Best! You'd never let rejection get in the way of reaching your goals. You're creative and open to new ideas, so there's no problem with taking some criticism to help perfect your amazing writing skills.

Destined To Be A Star

Destiny didn't stop singing after her disastrous first stage appearance. You can cope too – use rejection as fuel to keep going and show people what you **can** do. Don't be afraid to big up your best creative skills – being confident in your talent will help make your stories even better!

Brilliant Like Beauty

Beauty believed she was ugly and dull, but she developed a brilliant biscuit business! Even the most gifted writers have to deal with rejection, so don't let it get you down. Believe in **you** and keep going till you get that one 'yes' – It'll be the only answer that counts!

Write a Book Review

Become a book critic and write about the last book you read.

Here are some tips –

Say why you liked or didn't like it.

Talk about the characters you liked and disliked and why.

Was it exciting, scary or did it make you cry?

Did any of it make you laugh out loud?

Do you wish there was a sequel so you could find out what happens next?

Did it have a great ending or were you left feeling a little disappointed?

You'll be creating a best-seller in no time!
Super Story Starters
Stuck for a story idea? No problem!
Try these fun writing games!

Create a Great Character

Develop a main character in six simple steps! Just fill in the character profile with your answers!

4. Give your character a little more background. Where do they live and who with? Tick the choices you want and write in a little bit to describe each person.

1. Who or what will your character be? You don't have to choose a person — you could have a talking dog, an invisible elf or even a little raincloud. Write down a name and short description.

2. Now pick some words to describe your character like happy, mischievous, confused, spoiled-rotten or playful. Think of three words to use.

5. Write down three favourite things for your character and three things they dislike.

3. What does your character look like? If it's a person, what do they like to wear? Are they neat and tidy or scruffy and dirty? Do they have long hair, or green eyes? Choose another three words to describe your character's appearance.

6. Choose one thing to really make your character stand out. Maybe they have a special talent or even a super-power! What about an extremely bad temper? Perhaps they're absolutely terrified of something or they never utter a word, just like Lizzie Zipmouth.

Now you have a detailed character profile! Introduce your character by writing a short paragraph about them using your description. This is what Beauty says about her angry dad in *Cookie* —

Dad didn't just get cross. It was way way way more scary. He was like a volcano. You never quite knew when he'd erupt and explode and engulf you in molten lava.

Develop your story by creating a situation, event or problem for your character to experience, like their first day at school or being bored during the holidays. This will form the main plot and you'll be able to show how your character reacts or changes to this situation.

Follow this profile plan for all your story characters — you can make lots and keep them in a handy file, ready to use at any time!

My Character Profile

My character is called ....

My character is a ....

Three words to describe my character are

1 ....

2 ....

3 ....

My character's appearance

1 ....

2 ....

3 ....

My character lives..

....

- [ ] Alone or with
- [ ] Mum called .... She is ....
- [ ] Dad called .... He is ....
- [ ] Brothers ....
- [ ] Sisters ....
- [ ] Pets ....
- [ ] Friends ....

Three likes	Three dislikes
....	....
....	....
....	....

What makes my character stand out?

....

....

Ultimate Plot Planner

Story-writing made simple!

HOW TO PLAY

Roll a dice and match the number to pick a choice from each section and build your story!

A. Today I planned to...

1. take a long walk with
2. go shopping with
3. explore the woods with
4. go camping with
5. make a den with
6. play in the park with

B.

1. my bestie.
2. my identical twin.
3. the new girl at school.
4. my creepy neighbour.
5. my pesky brother.
6. a long-lost ancestor.

Play over and over to get lots of different storylines!

C. But then I heard that...

1. the local sweet shop was handing out freebies!
2. my mum was planning a special surprise for me.
3. the cinema was showing my fave film in 3D!
4. a mysterious letter had arrived addressed to me.
5. a local TV channel was filming right outside my house!
6. my friends were all going ice-skating.

D. So I...

1. ran all the way home.
2. made a phone call to my mates.
3. jumped on the next bus.
4. hailed a taxi at once.
5. begged my dad for a lift.
6. 'borrowed' my brother's scooter and headed off.

E. Just then, I saw...

1. a long, long queue of traffic!
2. my friends, waiting patiently for me.
3. the strictest teacher in school!
4. my favourite author, Jacqueline Wilson!
5. Dani Harmer, shopping with a friend!
6. my worst enemy and her gang.

F. So I...

1. ran away as fast as I could.
2. took a top-secret shortcut.
3. took a sneaky photo on my mobile.
4. hid behind a bush.
5. pulled my scarf over my face in a make-shift disguise.
6. waved cheerily and walked on by.

What's Your Perfect Story?

Horror, adventure or comedy — what will you write?

1. You're on a camping trip and hear a noise in the middle of the night. You...

A) Think it was an owl.

B) Get up to find out what it was.

C) Wake up your bezzie and spook each other senseless!

2. What's your ideal holiday location?

A) The mountains.

C) The beach.

B) An old castle.

3. You're shopping with Mum. What would you like to buy?

B) That quirky doll in the charity shop.

C) A DVD you can watch with your BFF.

A) A pair of trainers — you've worn your old ones through.

4. You're having a sleepover. You're going to...

A) Play Wii games and make tasty snacks.

C) Eat lots of popcorn and play truth or dare.

B) Camp in the back garden and tell ghost stories.

5. **In your diary you're most likely to write...**

A) I can't wait to go on holiday!
B) Can't sleep after watching that scary film!
C) The funniest thing happened in class today...

6. **Your BFF would describe you as...**

B) Smart and loyal.
A) Outgoing and friendly.
C) Playful and funny.

You answered...

Mostly A

You should write an *adventure novel!*
You're active, inquisitive and like a challenge - an adventure story would be perfect for you!

Try...

- Reading history books to find out about unusual people and locations.
- Including a dramatic scene.

Mostly B

You should write a *spooky story!*
You're drawn to the supernatural and love to be spooked - you're the ideal person to write a horror story!

Try...

- Making an everyday object scary.
- To build suspense over a long passage.

Mostly C

You should write a *clever comedy!*
You're always getting into hilarious situations and you love having a laugh with your mates. Why not try writing a comedy?

Try...

- Using your own embarrassing tale.
- Adding funny sound effects or slapstick.

Ghouls & Goosebumps!

Cut out and use the number and letter tiles from the bottom of the pages or copy them to make your own set. Put them in bowls and pick when needed.

1. Choose your favourite colour to pick a brave and bold hero/heroine for your tale.

- Courageous Connie
- Daring Daz
- Georgie, ghoul–hunter extraordinaire
- Fearless Freda
- Valerie the Valiant
- Muscly Mike
- Monster–Masher Maud
- Selina the Spectre–Slayer

2. Pick out a number tile to choose a suitably spooky location where your story unfolds...

1 A dusty attic, crammed with antique furniture draped in sheets.

2 The echoing bell tower of an ancient church.

3 Amongst the crooked gravestones of a moonlit cemetery.

4 In the dimly–lit hallway of an imposing mansion.

5 Aboard a rickety boat in the middle of the ocean, far from land.

6 Lost in the thick of a deep, dark forest.

7 Imprisoned in the dungeons of a ruined castle.

8 Wandering a maze of underground tunnels, armed only with a flickering torch.

9 Exploring ancient catacombs and pyramids in Egypt.

1	2	3	4	5	6	7	8	9

3. Something goes bump in the night! Pick a letter tile to find out who, or what (eek!), your hero/heroine will stumble across...

S — Slithering snakes

C — Crusty Egyptian mummy

A — Aggressive werewolf

R — Rotten zombie

Y — Yeti!

G — Gunge-dripping ghost

H — Hairy monster

O — One-eyed witch

U — UFO

L — Lady Blood, the vampire

4. Your hero/heroine must fight, face their fears and defeat the enemy! Roll a dice to find a weapon of choice...

1 Silver sword of destiny

2 Spell to be chanted three times

3 Laser-shooting space gun

4 Hypnotising powers

5 Magic wand

6 Jewelled dagger

Will they live scarily-ever-after? Or will they meet a gory and gruesome end? Have fun writing a tantalising, terror-filled ending to your story!

S	C	A	R	Y	G	H	O	U	L

Lotsa Little

Fun stuff to brighten a boring day!

Which JW Book Should You Read?

Follow the arrows to pick a new book!

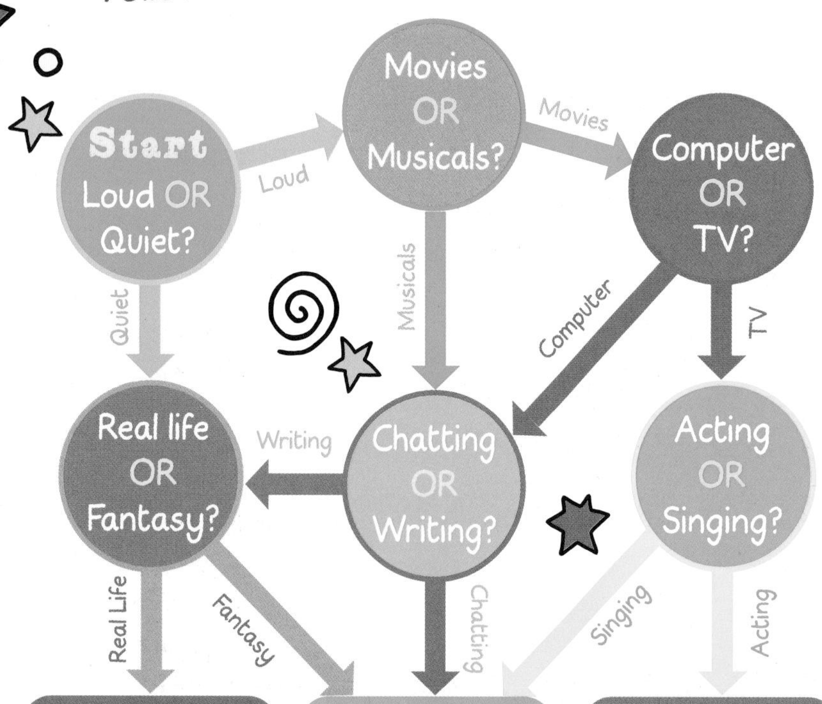

Grab the tissues! You love reading sad stories. Is there a happy ending? We can't spoil the surprise!

You're hooked on shows like the X Factor and finding out the latest star gossip. The story of Destiny and Sunset has lots of celebrity style for you.

There's so much drama and excitement in Hetty Feather's latest adventure as she sets out to find her father. Drama Queens like you need to read this book!

Find A Fun Activity!

You ❤

1 Magazines

What's inside

1 Recipes

2 Stories

For a birthday

1 Restaurant

The best thing

1 Midnight feasts

2 Creepy stories

1 – 4 Brilliant Baking

5 – 8 Super Story Writing

9 – 12 Awesome Artworks

Quizzes!

Circle where you fit on the grid then add up your numbers to reveal all...

...to collect...

2 Books — 3 Stationery

...your notebooks?

3 Drawings

...treat you'd love...

2 Cinema — 3 Craft party

...about sleepovers is...

3 Making invites

Get busy making some beautiful cookies or cakes for your friends and family.

There's always a new idea buzzing around your brain so get scribbling — it could be the next best seller!

You love arts and crafts, so make a cool collage, get painting or sketch your favourite JW characters.

What's Your Creative Career?

Answer these questions to find out!

1. WHICH OF THESE WOULD MAKE YOU MOST NERVOUS?
   - Doing a talk in front of your class
   - Entering an art competition
   - Writing a story for homework

2. YOU'RE A BRILLIANT BESTIE BECAUSE...
   - You love to make gifts for your friends
   - You keep your pals laughing with jokes and fun
   - You're always happy to help out with a problem

3. YOU HAVE AN HOUR TO DO ANYTHING YOU LIKE. DO YOU
   - Design an outfit for yourself?
   - Fill in your diary or scrapbook?
   - Chat to your BF on the phone?

4. YOU HAVE £10 TO SPEND. WHAT DO YOU BUY?
   - Credit for your phone or a voucher for your iPod
   - Paints and craft stuff
   - A fabulous, sparkly notebook and pen

5. YOU'RE MOST LIKELY TO BE TOLD OFF FOR...
   - Drawing and doodling on everything
   - Not paying attention in class
   - Constant chatter

You chose...

MOSTLY BLUE –
WRITER
You have a fabulous imagination and could spend all day making up stories.
YOUR TASK: Start a book club with your BFs to share your favourite tales.

MOSTLY PINK –
ARTIST
You're awesome at art! You love creating pictures for your besties.
YOUR TASK: Draw some of your own illustrations for your favourite book.

MOSTLY PURPLE –
BOOK AGENT
You're confident, like meeting new people and love to chat. You'd be great at persuading people to publish stories and books.
YOUR TASK: Do a project on your favourite author for your next school talk.

Exceptional	Tremendous	Easy-peasy
Wonderful	Terrific	Brilliant

How To Play!

On your own:

- Every time you land on a star take a word from the bowl.
- When you finish write a story about Tracy using every word.

With others:

- Cut out the words from the bottom of the page or copy them onto paper.
- Fold them up and pop into a bowl.
- Use coins or badges as counters.
- Roll the dice to move and follow the instructions on each square you land on.
- Every time you land on a star pick up a word from the bowl.
- You must make up a sentence using the word before you can move on.

Why Not?

Write out more of your own marvellous mammoth words to add to the game!

Beautifully	Idiotic	Hideous
Institutionalised	Enhanced	Stupendous

Random Renamer!

Making a silly story title is as easy as 1, 2, 3!

Make one selection from each section then put them together to reveal your title.

1

- My Friend
- A Stranger
- Dogs
- An Enemy
- I
- The Girl
- Gangs
- Ballerinas
- The Teacher
- Fluffy Kittens
- Umbrellas

2

- Confiscated
- Burped
- Ran Off With
- Lurked In
- Cleaning
- Sparkled
- Knitted
- Squished
- Twisted
- Threw Away

3

- The Train
- Fluffy Spotty Socks
- Purple Tomatoes
- Dark Clouds
- Yesterday
- The Lunchbox
- Bananas
- Silver Shoes
- Paper Tissues
- A Bin Bag

My silly story title is

____

____

Imagine If...
Your next creation is only a day-dream away!
Get your brain cells jumping!
POW!

Tracy FACT or FIB

Tracy can tell lots of tall tales but which of these are true and which are false?

1.

When I was born I had beautiful silky, fair hair, just like my mum's. But when I was about six months old, I had a terrible allergic reaction to bananas and my hair began to grow in dark and wild.

FACT ☐ FIB ☐

2.

When I played the Dare Game with Justine–Sad–Loser–Littlewood I ate *two* worms, ran across the garden naked and climbed an incredibly tall tree. When I played the Dare Game with Football and Alexander, I put my knickers on top of a tree like a little frilly flag!

FACT ☐ FIB ☐

3.

After doing a Very Bad Thing at school my headteacher, Mrs Darlow, made me polish the hall floor as punishment. I had to stay behind for half an hour each night till it was all done. Honestly, she treated me like an unpaid skivvy.

FACT ☐ FIB ☐

4.

I've won a few prizes in my time, like a karaoke machine and a posh day out. But my biggest prize ever was a million pounds on a lottery ticket I *borrowed* from Cam's purse. I just haven't told anyone yet because I don't want to be adored by all for my money alone.

FACT ☐ FIB ☐

Beaker FIB?

6. I'm an Amazing Actress, just like my mum, Carly (she lives in Hollywood, which is why I don't see her much). I was Quite Incredible playing the part of Scrooge in *A Christmas Carol.*

FACT ☐ FIB ☐

5. When I moved out of the Dumping Ground I went to live with Cam in a swanky penthouse apartment. I have everything a girl could wish for — designer shoes, gadgets galore and heaps of presents. Plus she lets me do *Whatever I Want.*

FACT ☐ FIB ☐

7. Elaine the Pain (my annoying social worker) often uses the following words to describe lovely, lovely me –

- ☑ Adorable
- ☑ Darling
- ☑ Sweetheart
- ☑ Obedient
- ☑ Precious
- ☑ Delightful

FACT ☐

FIB ☐

8. On my birthday there's nothing I love more than sharing my cake with Peter Ingham and the rest of the Dumping Ground gang. I don't mind *one teeny, tiny bit* watching them all tuck into the fluffy sponge and yummy icing. In fact, just thinking about sharing gives me a Warm and Generous glow.

FACT ☐ FIB ☐

9. I lived with my mum when I was little and we got on great, but then she got this Monster Gorilla Boyfriend and I hated him and he hated me back and beat me up and so I had to be taken into care.

FACT ☐ FIB ☐

10. I have never, ever, *ever* used the following unkind descriptions –

- ☑ Weedy Peter
- ☑ Mrs Vomit Bagley
- ☑ Justine–Absolutely–Ugly–Littlewood
- ☑ Stupid social worker

FACT ☐ FIB ☐

Answers: 1. Fib 2. Fact 3. Fact 4. Fib 5. Fib 6. Fact 7. Fib 8. Fib 9. Fact 10. Fib

Who Said It?

Jacky uses her imagination to come up with hundreds of different characters!

Can you work out which books these quotes come from? Give yourself extra points if you can also name the characters who said it!

1. I have a pet. She is a tabby cat called Mabel. I love her dearly. But she is very, very, very *boring*. She doesn't do anything. She just sleeps.

Character: ....

Book: ....

2. It didn't matter if she was mad or bad. She belonged to us and we belonged to her. The three of us. Marigold and Star and Dolphin.

Character: ....

Book: ....

3. If I could only get a job I could eat Big Macs and French fries every day and wear designer from top to toe, yeah, especially my footwear, and buy all the videos and computer games I want and take trips to Disneyland.

Character: ....

Book: ....

4. I walked left–right, left–right, like a little soldier, though my leg ached worse than ever. We got the bus to the hospital — *two* buses — and although I usually thought a bus ride was a treat and liked chatting to the conductor, this time I kept quiet and nibbled my lip anxiously the whole way.

Character: ....

Book: ....

5. They were amazing clothes too, a tiny black lace top, a silver and white embroidered waistcoat, a purple velvet tiered skirt edged with crimson lace, and black pointy Goth boots with high heels. She had brightly coloured Indian bangles jingling all the way up both arms and beads plaited into her hair.

Character: ....

Book: ....

6. Or we copy everything twice... two lots of sums, two maps, two fact–sheets, because we say everything's got to be doubled because we're a double ourselves. 'Double trouble', says Dumbo Debenham.

Character: ....

Book: ....

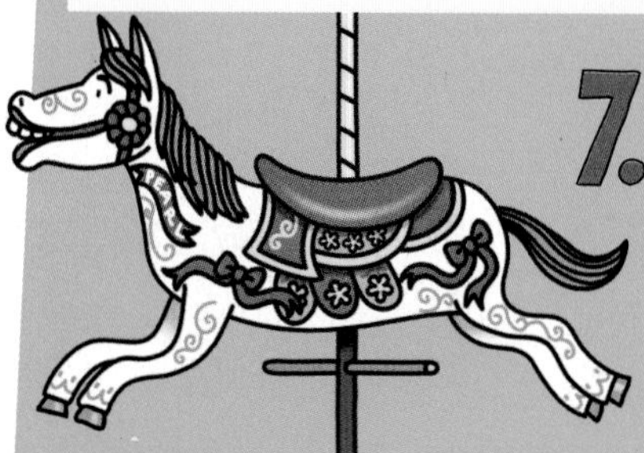

7. School was heavenly now I was sitting next to Susan. I even enjoyed maths. Well, I didn't exactly *enjoy* it, but it was quite companionable having Susan go through each sum with me and tell me what to do.

Character: ....

Book: ....

8. I wanted to keep out of Dad's way when he came home from golf but he started bellowing for me the moment he got in the front door. I didn't dare lurk in my room. I didn't want him thudding up the stairs and bursting into my bedroom. If he saw my broken mirror he'd explode.

Character: ....

Book: ....

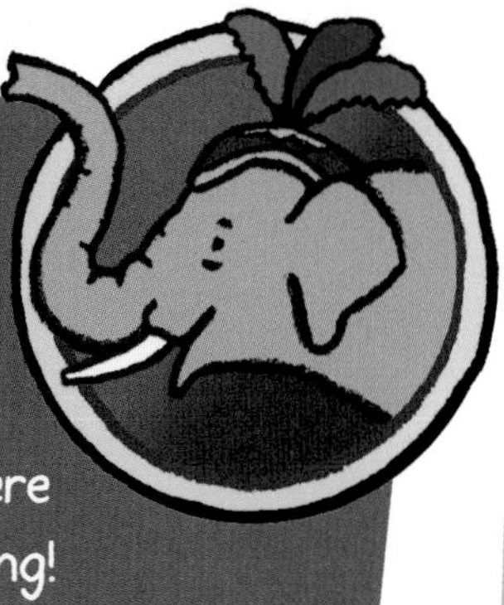

9. I hesitated. Where were my new undergarments? I saw something white in my basket, but it was simply a strange old–fashioned cap. There was no shift, no drawers, nothing!

Character: ....

Book: ....

10. She leaves a little pink trail around the house — sparkly slides and ribbons and notebooks. You breathe in her revolting scent long after she's gone off to hang out at her friends' houses. She's not allowed to wear real perfume yet, but she's got this rose hand cream that smells really strongly.

Character: ....

Book: ....

Answers: 1. Verity, *The Cat Mummy* 2. Dolphin, *The Illustrated Mum* 3. Tracy Beaker, *The Dare Game* 4. Elsie, *Queenie* 5. Violet, *Midnight* 6. Ruby, *Double Act* 7. Floss, *Candyfloss* 8. Beauty, *Cookie* 9. Hetty, *Hetty Feather* 10. Marty, *The Worst Thing About My Sister*

Andy's Amazing New Life

In *The Suitcase Kid*, Andy longs to return to Mulberry Cottage where she can live the perfect life with Mum, Dad and her tiny toy rabbit, Radish. Let's imagine a dream life for her.

Hurray! After sharing with her horrid step-sister Katie, Andy is finally getting her own bedroom! Help her create a fabulous design...

Andy enjoyed her model shoot very much, even if she did feel a bit silly doing it. Would she like to have a huge wardrobe full of glam clothes?

Or will she have a nice desk and comfy chair where she can sit down and write down her innermost secrets?

What type of bed will she have? A king-sized, four-poster bed all to herself with posh velvet pillows and beautiful bed linens?

Or maybe a set of bunk beds so she and Radish can each have a bed to themselves?

What about a fancy round bed? You choose!

Will Andy make a cute new house for Radish so she can live in luxury too?

Decorate the window with gorgeous curtains or funky blinds!

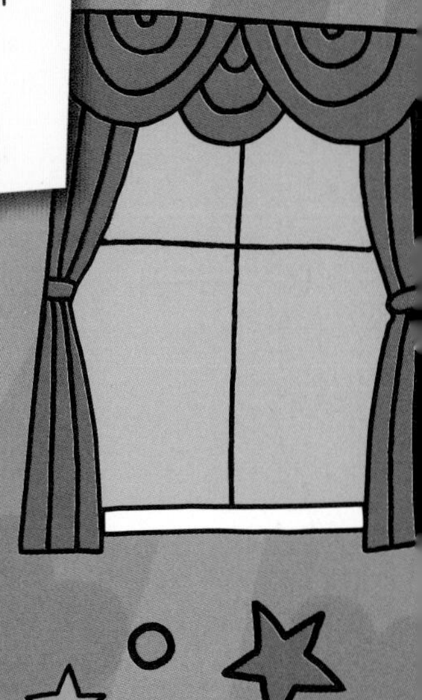

What will be on the walls? Perhaps Andy will use posters of her favourite things, or have rows and rows of books all lined up on pretty shelves.

Will she put up family photos or the pictures her dad took of her dressed as a model?

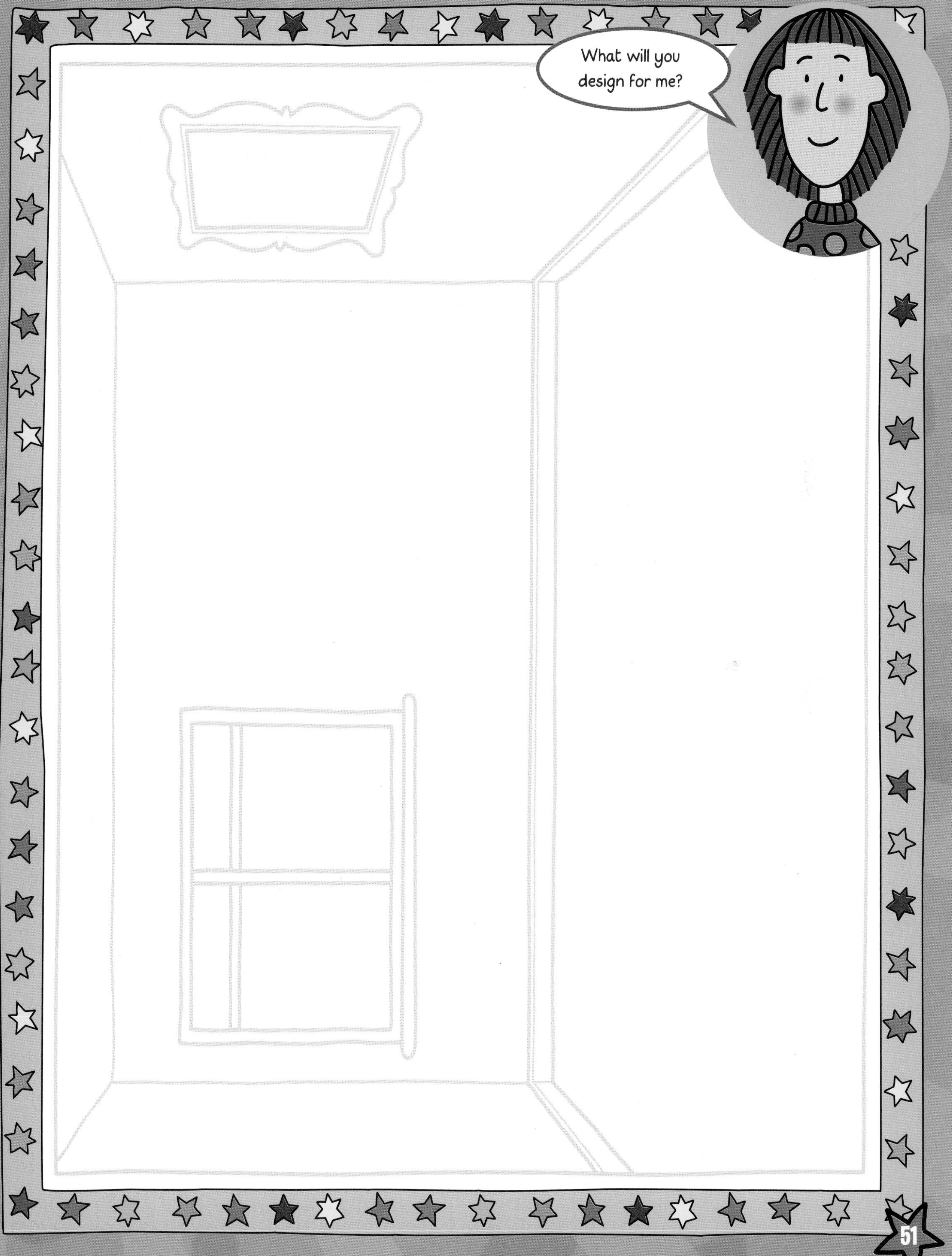
What will you design for me?

Andy's Amazing New Life

Can you design a luxury lounge for Andy?

No matter where Andy stays, with either her mum's new family or her dad's, there are always lots of people running around. All she wants is some space to herself with no one to disturb her.

What sort of furniture would Andy love – something sleek and modern, glitzy and glam, or comfy and casual? Which would Radish prefer?

Will they have a giant squishy sofa with heaps of plump cushions or will they lounge around on beanbags and fluffy rugs?

What colours will Andy choose? Something restful and calm or bright shades like aqua blue and tropical pink?

Will there be lots of plants so she can play games of hide and seek with Radish?

Would Andy love the glamour of glittering accessories like a huge crystal chandelier and lots of mirrors? Or maybe she'd prefer fun touches like a swinging hammock, table tennis and video games.

Will she have a giant TV and amazing computer? What about a super-cool music set-up so Andy can dance till she drops? Her mean stepsister would be soooo jealous!

Why not create a fabulous collage with pictures cut out of old magazines or catalogues?

Andy's Amazing New Life

Create a new supermodel look!

Andy felt like a film star the day her dad took lots of photographs of her dressed up in fancy frocks and makeup. But how would you dress her for another model makeover?

Andy had her hair twisted into a bun for her fashion model shoot. Is this a good look for her? What about curls or coloured extensions? Maybe she'd suit braids or a long, swishy side ponytail.

Will Andy wear another glitzy long dress or will she model something more modern like a funky t-shirt with a cool slogan?

She might suit designs like stars, stripes or a skull and crossbones. Will there be a special little pocket somewhere for Radish to hide in? You could give Radish a new outfit too!

For makeup, Andy had dark eyeshadow and purple lipstick. Would you try something different? What about emerald green shadow or light pink and gold? You even could give her flicked eyeliner and fluttering false lashes!

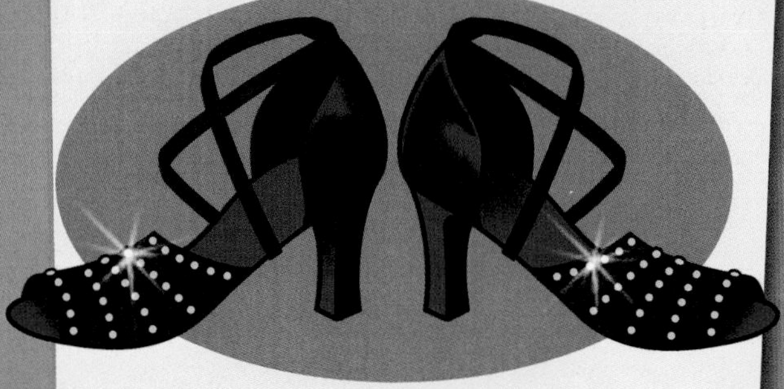

Choose shoes you think Andy will like. Will she have on pretty strappy sandals or something like glam and sparkly high heels? Maybe she'd love some specially customised Converse boots.

Go wild with Andy's accessories. She could wear chunky rings like Jacky's, lots of bangles, a glittering gemstone necklace or some stunning diamond earrings. Will she carry a pretty bag, or accessorise with something cute like pins and badges? What about a daring temporary tattoo?

Start sketching! Why not stick on some fabric or gems too?

Let's imagine... Let's imagine... Let's imagine... Let's imagine... Let's imagine... Let's imagine.

Imagine If...

What would happen if Jacky's characters met each other?

...Beauty met Sunset

She could make some of her brilliant bunny cookies for Sunset's birthday party.

...Jodie met Vicky Angel

They could swap and share outfits and fashion tips.

...Tracy met Mandy

She could introduce Black Belt Tracy to Mandy's evil bully Kim!

Let's imagine... Let's imagine... Let's imagine... Let's imagine... Let's imagine... Let's imagine...

...Dolphin met Hetty

Hetty could sew a beautiful new embroidered dress for Dolphin so she didn't get laughed at at school.

...Lily met Andy

They could design their perfect home and share each other's problems and worries.

...Biscuits met Elsa

They could play pranks and laugh all day long at jokes.

Which of Jacky's characters do you think should meet up?

Write about them and what they'd get up to here —

. . . .

. . . .

. . . .

. . . .

. . . .

. . . .

. . . .

Let's imagine... Let's imagine... Let's imagine... Let's imagin... imagine.

What Happens Next?

Do you ever wonder what happens to the characters after you finish a book? Why not try writing your own ending for *Little Darlings*?

Here are some questions to get you thinking –

What will happen between Sunset's mum, Suzy, and Destiny's mum? Can they ever be friends?

Will Sunset and Destiny get together to become a famous singer/songwriter team?

Do you think Danny will ever accept Destiny as his own?

How will Sweetie and Ace behave as they grow older?

Will Sunset's mum and dad be able to work out their differences?

Will Sunset become more confident and learn to love the red carpet lifestyle?

There are so many things that could happen! Help plan out your story by jotting down some ideas here –

Makes & Bakes!

Impress your friends and family!

You'll need:

Felt or old fabric
Button
Ribbon
Needle
Thread
Cotton wool or old tights for stuffings

Honey Bunny Bag Charm

1. Trace the bunny pattern on page 88 and cut a pattern from paper. Put the two felt squares together and pin on the pattern. Cut round the pattern to make two bunny heads.

2. Take one bunny head and sew the heart-shaped button on the middle of the face. Now stitch or draw a black mouth and eyes like this.

3. Put the two heads together again. Fold the ribbon in half and tuck it in here. Tightly stitch it in place.

4.

Now sew round the edges with a small running or blanket stitch (there's a How to Blanket Stitch on page 88). Leave a small space open at the chin for stuffing.

5.

Stuff the bunny with a little cotton wool. Use a pencil to push it into the long ears. Stitch up the gap.

Why not?

Alter the bunny pattern to make a cat or dog charm.

6.

Add a felt flower and pink ears to your bunny like this. To finish, attach the key ring to the ribbon loop.

Why not?

Make more bunnies for your besties.

Five-minute Makeovers

Turn a boring boy t-shirt into hot holiday clothes!

YOU'LL NEED:

- Old baggy
- t-shirts
- Ribbon
- Scissors

Slouchy Top

- Cut away the neck.
- Cut the hemmed edges from the sleeves and put aside.
- Cut diagonally from the outside edge of the sleeve to the underarm seam like this.

Cut a slit along the top edge of each sleeve. Stop about 2–3cm from the shoulder seam.

Tie knots in the sleeves like this

Measure 10cm up from the bottom of the t-shirt and make two tiny snips at the sides

Cut the stitching to open out the sleeve hems like this.

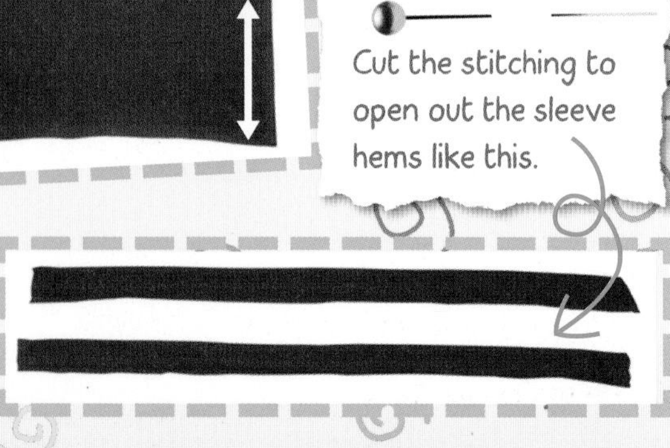

- Cut the neck into a wider slash.
- Add some cute badges!

- Bunch up the hem of the t-shirt and tie the strips in a knot.
- Pull each sleeve hem strip halfway through the snipped holes.

- Wear it over a plain vest with your leggings.
- Perfect for dance class!

Pretty Summer Dress

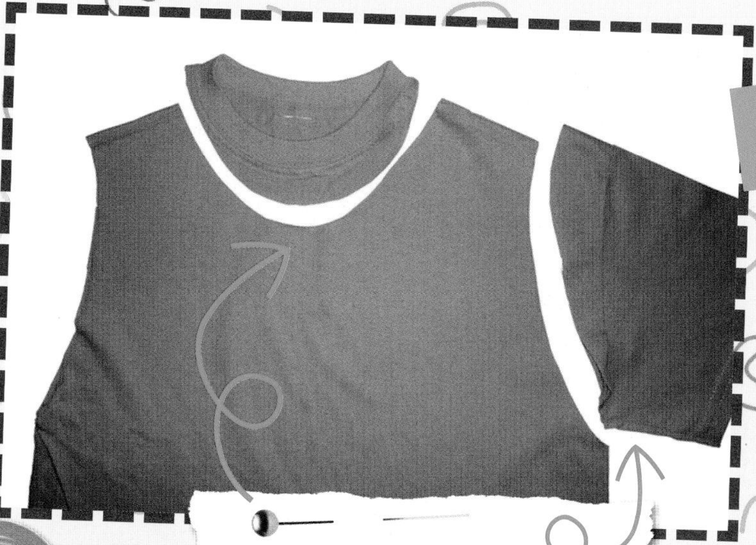

- Cut out the neck.
- Cut out the sleeves and lay aside.

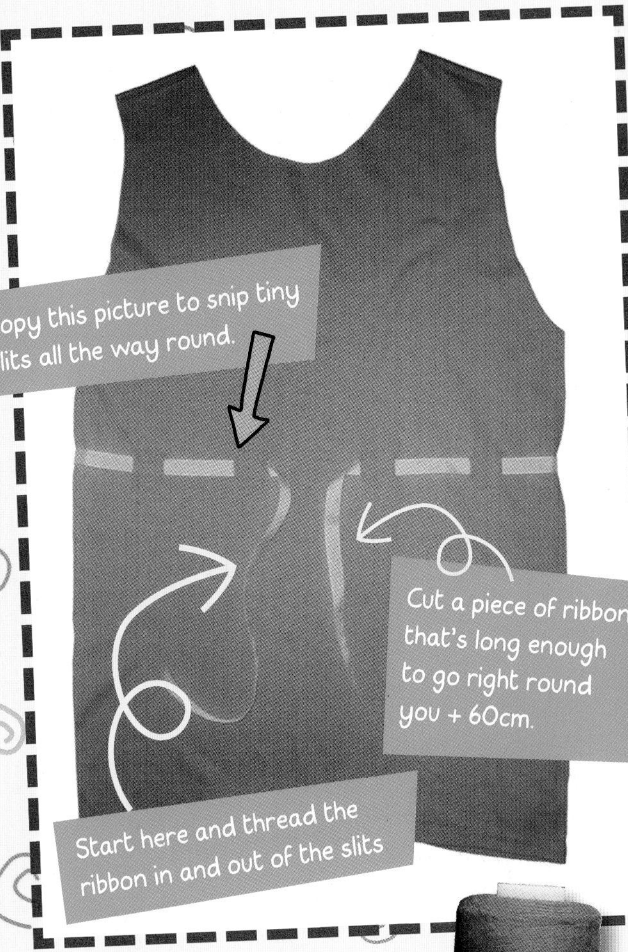

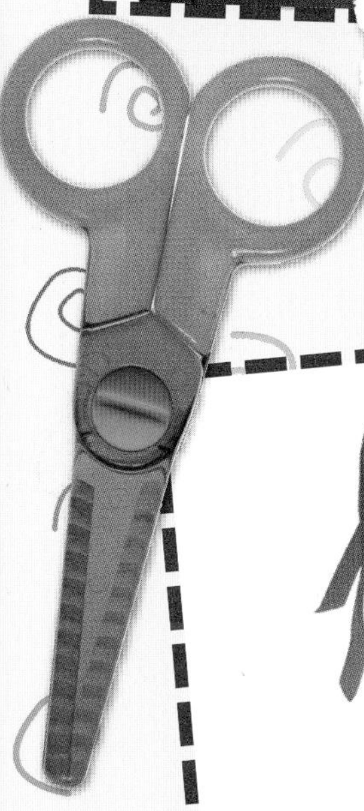

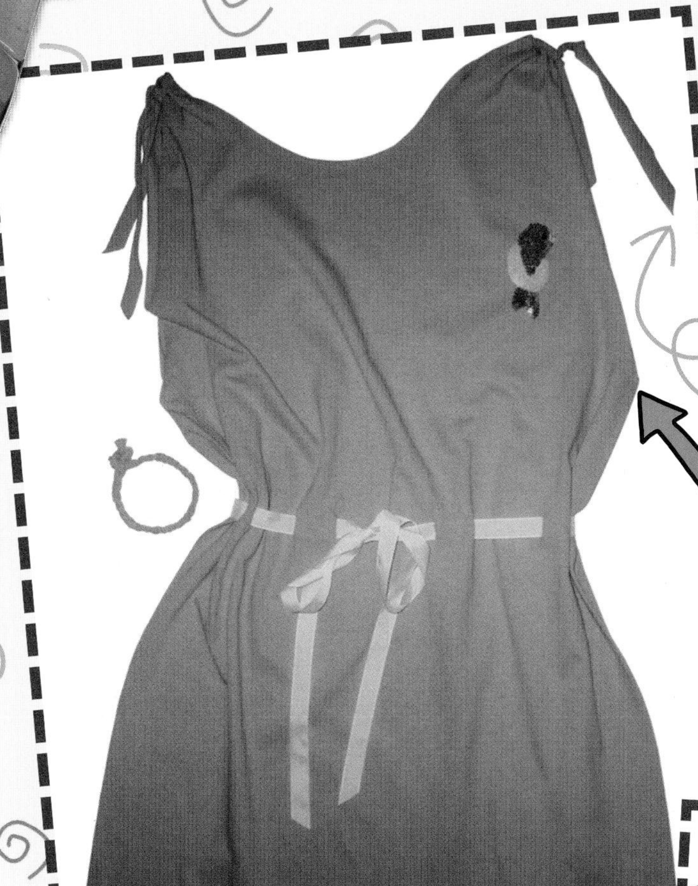

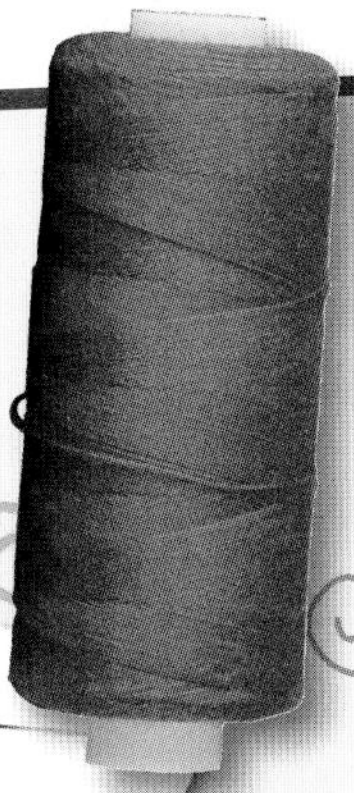

- Pull and tie at the waist.
- Cut two narrow strips from the sleeves and tie at the shoulders like this.
- If this seam is too low, wear your dress over a strappy vest top.

TIP!
Keep the sleeve hems to use as hair bobbles at the beach or pool — they won't snag wet hair!

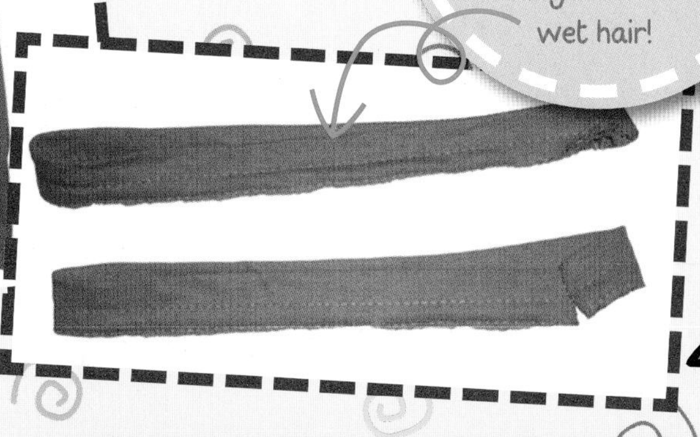

Bow Back Top

- Cut out the neck.
- Cut away the sleeves as shown.

Cut a narrow strip from each sleeve and put aside.

TIP! Fold the t-shirt in half down the centre and cut both at once so the sides match.

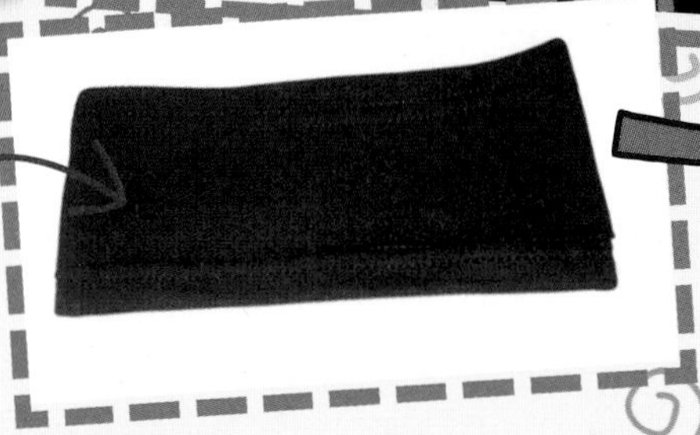

- Take the two hemmed sleeve pieces and tuck one inside the other. Now both sides will have a hemmed edge.

- Cut the ribbed neckband away from any remaining material or stitching.
  Snip to open it into a strip, wrap tightly round the sleeve pieces to create a bow shape and knot tightly at the back.

- Cut a strip from any leftover fabric and push it under the knot like this.

Take the narrow bands left from the sleeves, snip to make strips and tie at the shoulders.

Turn the top to the back and tie on the bow to gather up the fabric like this.

TIP! Make the bow sparkle with some stick-on gems.

Make Matching Bracelets

- Cut three narrow bands from the sleeve.
- Open into strips and knot together at the top. Trim the ends of the knot.

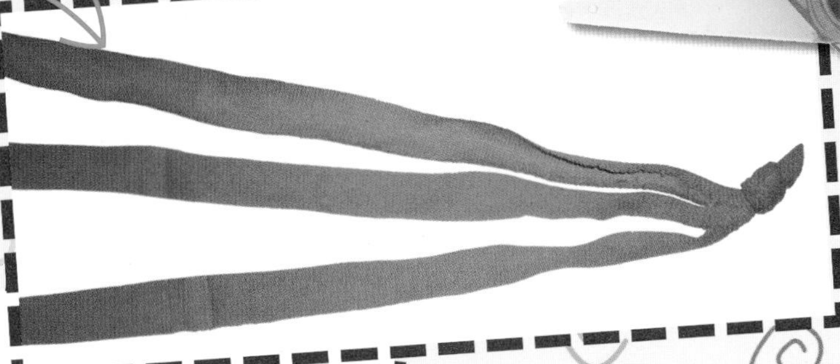

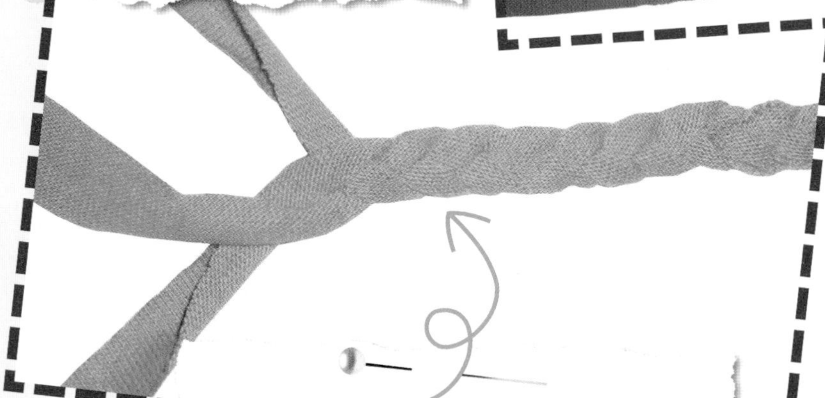

Start to braid the strips and keep going till you have enough to wrap round your wrist. Braid an extra 1.5cm then tie in a tight knot. Trim off any leftover fabric.

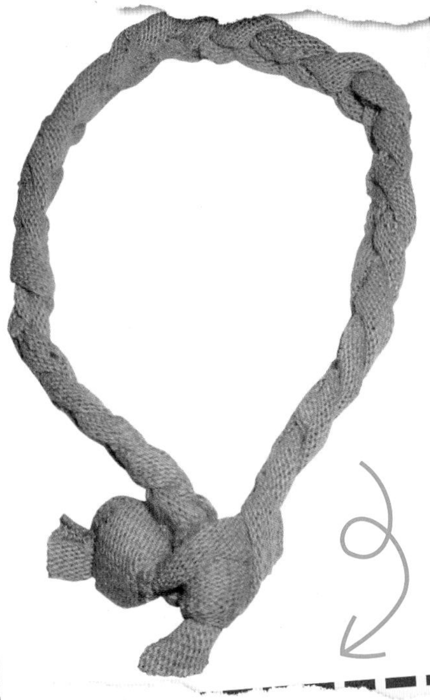

Fasten on by pushing the first knot through the last bit of your braiding like this. They're stretchy so you can pull them on and off without unfastening.

Skull Stencil

Use this stencil to rock your bow back top!

- Trace it on to paper then cut out the shape.
- Pin to the front of your top and use glitter glue or puffy paints to create the outline.
- Buttons make great eyes!

Cheeky Chicks!

You'll need:

- 12 fairy cakes
- 1 tub of ready-made frosting
- 1 pack of yellow candy melts (from Hobbycraft or Amazon)
- Yellow or orange mini sugar beans
- Heart & flower-shaped cake sprinkles
- Black food colour pen
- Lolly sticks
- Green sweet cases (optional)

1. Make cake balls by crumbling the fairy cakes into a bowl. Next, stir in a little of the frosting at a time until the mix is sticky enough to roll into balls.

Roll into small balls and chill in the fridge for 2 hours or freezer for 30 minutes.

2. Follow the pack instructions to melt the candy melts in a bowl — ask an adult to help. Stir in a teaspoon of vegetable oil.

Attach each lolly stick by dipping one end into the melted candy and then pushing into a chilled cake ball. Pop back in the fridge to set.

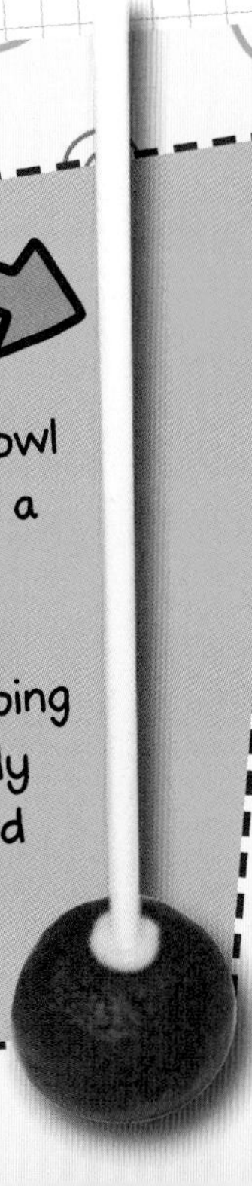

3.

Re-melt the candy then dip in each cake pop, swirl around to cover all sides and gently tap off any excess coating.

4.

While the coating is still wet gently place on two yellow sugar bean wings, an orange sugar bean beak and two little flower sprinkle feet.

Make hair bows for the girls with heart shaped sprinkles. Stand in a cup to dry.

5.

When the coating is completely dry you can finish by drawing on eyes with the black food colour pen.

Why not?

Make some grass for your chicks to sit on. Fold a sweet case into quarters and snip off the tiny corner. Cut the top into a curved petal then push on to the pop stick.

How to Make Basic Cookie Dough

You'll need:

- 90g butter or margarine
- 100g caster sugar
- 1 egg
- 200g plain flour
- ½ teaspoon salt
- ½ teaspoon baking powder
- 1 teaspoon vanilla essence

1. Mix the butter and sugar together until light and fluffy. Mix in the egg and vanilla essence.

2. Add the salt and baking powder to the flour and sift into the butter sugar mix. Stir together to get a soft dough.

3. Turn out on to a floured surface and shape the dough into a smooth circle. Wrap in cling film and chill in the fridge for at least 30 minutes before using.

Set the oven to 180°C.

To make the cookies you'll need:

- Basic cookie dough
- Bag of hard fruity sweets
- 100g icing sugar
- Food colouring
- Sprinkles

1. Roll out the dough to around 5mm thick and cut out your biscuits. Place them on a baking tray lined with greaseproof paper. Now carefully cut a circle or smaller shape from the centre.

Bake for 10 minutes.

2. Meanwhile, place some unwrapped fruit sweets in a plastic bag. Wrap the bag in a tea towel and smash the sweets into small pieces with a rolling pin.

Take out the partly baked cookies — ask an adult to help with the hot oven.

Crystal Gem Cookies

3. Fill the centre holes with the broken sweets and pop back in for another 5 – 8 minutes till the cookies are pale gold. The sweets will melt to form a magical crystal gem in the middle!

Leave the cookies to cool on the baking tray before carefully peeling away the paper.

TIP!

Pack the finished cookies in a pretty box for the perfect prezzie!

4. Make some icing by mixing a little water with the icing sugar till you get a thick paste. If you want to colour it you only need to add a drop or two of colouring.

5. Use a knife dipped in warm water to carefully spread the icing on the cookies and add your sprinkles to finish. Lovely!

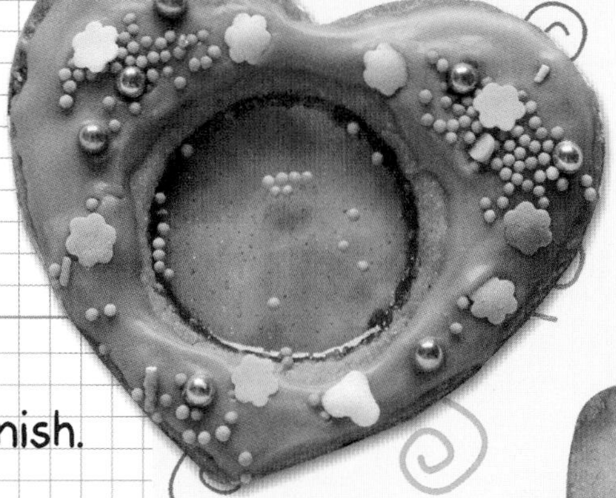

WHY NOT?

Leave off the icing and sprinkle the warm biscuits with caster sugar for a quick tea-time treat!

Always ask an adult before using any kitchen equipment.

Blah to Bling!

Transform a plain journal! This one has handy little pockets for pens and notes, plus another on the back for storing your photos and mementoes.

You'll need:

- Hardback notebook
- Cardboard tubes
- Scraps of paper (left-over wrapping paper is perfect)
- Ribbon or string
- Brown envelope
- Glue stick
- Double-sided sticky tape
- Stickers and gems
- Paper fastener

Start by tearing some scraps of paper. Stick them to the cover of the notebook, layering and overlapping to get a scrapbook effect.

Fold or trim the scraps round the edge of the book to get a neat finish.

Cut a little name tag to stick on.

Tip! Use foam pads to attach the tag for a 3D effect.

Cut some paper tubes to size and squash them flat. Cover them with paper — take care to wrap the paper round one open end to create a pocket. They don't have to be neat on the back. Stick the tube pockets to the front of the book with double-sided sticky tape.

FRONT

Add some sticker, gem and ribbon or string trims.

Choose a brown envelope that opens along the top like this.

Punch a hole.

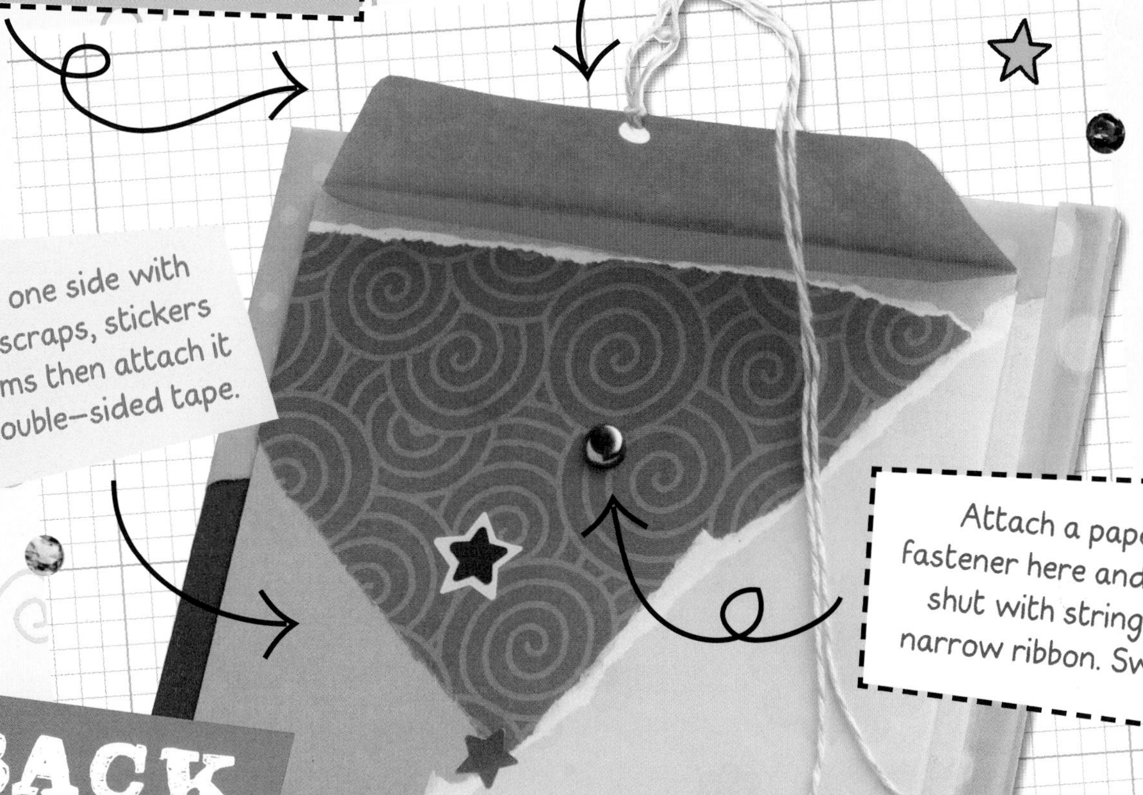

Cover one side with paper scraps, stickers and gems then attach it with double-sided tape.

Attach a paper fastener here and tie it shut with string or narrow ribbon. Sweet!

BACK

Why not?
Use favourite photos instead of sticker decorations.

Rag Bunting

Turn old stuff into lovely new stuff!

YOU'LL NEED...

- Old fabric — pillowcases, clothes and duvet covers are ideal
- String or ribbon

1 Tear the fabric into lots of long strips and fold each strip in half.

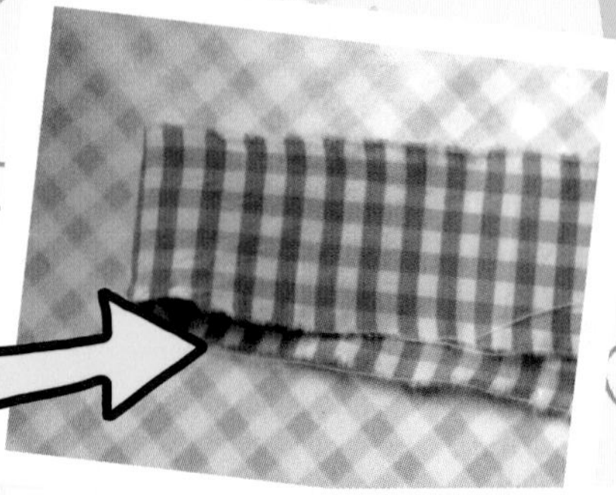

2 Place the string over the folded fabric like this.

3 Pass the raggy ends up through the loop and pull tight. That's it — just add as many strips as you like.

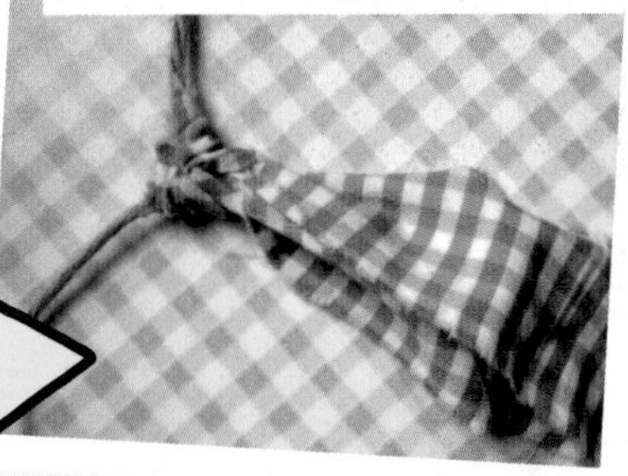

TIP!

Snip the edge of the fabric with scissors to make it easier to tear.

Hang in your room or garden.

Gorgeous!

Amazing Art!
Sketch and design with me!
Colour in Tracy!
ULTIMATE artist tricks and tips!

How to Draw Jacky... Then!

It's young Jacky! Sketch her in four easy steps!

1 Draw the oval of Jacky's chin and her ears. Add the curve of her face at one side and the wiggly line of her hair at the other.

Sketch in Jacky's neck and the collar of her blouse. Add the curved lines of her arms like this

2 Draw in two shoulder straps for Jacky's pinafore. Sketch the front of the pinafore with a slightly wavy hemline.

Copy the picture to add Jacky's legs and the outline of her shoes.

3 Now it's time to add Jacky's facial features and short wavy hair. Sketch the cuffs of her blouse and hands. Draw lines for her little white knee socks and the strap detail on her shoes.

4 Add the finishing touches by drawing the checked pattern on Jacky's pinafore and colour her in.

Jacky also longed for stylish and sparkly outfits to replace the rather prim clothes bought for her by her mum, Biddy.

Design a fabulous party outfit you think Jacky would love.

TIP!

Don't forget it's the 1950s – find out what fashions were like before starting your creation.

How to Draw Jacky... Now!

Sketch the Jacky we know and love! Nick shows you how...

1 Draw a tilted oval for Jacky's cheek and chin then add one ear. Sketch in the zig-zags of her spiky hair.

Add Jacky's neck and the curve of her top. Sketch her arms and add a bangle to each cuffline. Draw the rectangle of her body.

2 Give Jacky some more bangles then sketch in her hands. Draw on her glasses.

3 Sketch Jacky's facial expression then start to add the fine details — a glam necklace, patterns on her skirt and bangles, fabulous high heels and her famous, chunky rings!

4 Now add some colour to your drawing — Jacky loves black, but she also likes navy, silver and beautiful jewel shades like peacock blue and royal purple.

Nick's Tip!

Jacky needs a new outfit for a book launch party.

Design something for her to wear here –

SECRETS REVEALED!

Inside Nick's

THE BOSS

That's me!

MEET JOAN!

It can get pretty lonely when I'm busy working away. It's a good thing I have Joan, my shop dummy, to keep me company! She's looking especially glamorous in this brightly-printed dress!

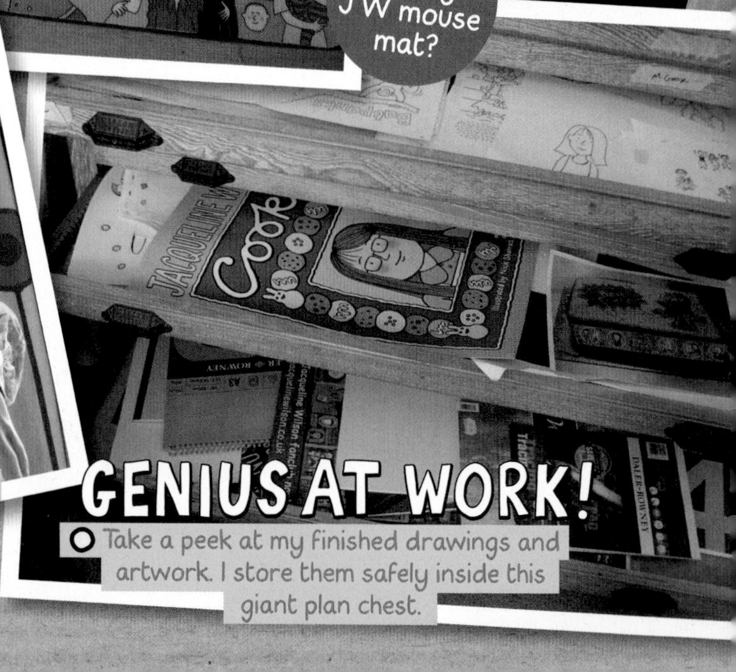

GENIUS AT WORK!

Take a peek at my finished drawings and artwork. I store them safely inside this giant plan chest.

Studio

MY DESK

Oops — I really should've tidied up before inviting you in! My office is always a little untidy but I think I work best surrounded by my favourite things.

HOME COMFORTS

I'm glad I work at home because I can wear my favourite pair of slippers to the office!

MY TOP TOOLS

I couldn't work without...

1 JACKY'S BOOKS

I read each story carefully to build up a clear picture of the characters in my head.

2 MY REFERENCE BOOKS

I often flick through my library of books for inspiration or if I need to get the details of a drawing just right — like Hetty's Victorian foundling costume or Madame Berenice's intricate turban.

3 PAINTS, PENS AND PENCILS

Although I do most of my work on a computer, I still like to sketch and scribble my ideas on paper first.

Now turn over to design your own dream art studio!

Design Your Dream Studio!

Wish you had a studio like Nick's? Create it here!

First things first, decide where your studio is going to be. Is it a room in your home like Nick's studio? Will you have a swanky loft in a converted warehouse? Or will it be a beachside hut that will provide you with lots of inspiration?
Write where it is here:

Is your studio bright and airy or small and cosy?

What about the décor? Is it sleek and modern so you can focus on your artwork, or is it a mish–mash of styles to keep you inspired?
Write about it here:

Do you have a pet or a mascot like Joan to keep you company?

Nick has lots of reference books in his studio, as well as lots of paints, pens and pencils. Will you have these things in your studio? If so, where will they go? Note down what kind of things you'll have here:

Now it's time to design your dream studio — use your notes to help you sketch your studio in the space below!

What can you see from the window of your studio? Beautiful countryside, a busy city, or something else?

What Type Of Artist

Your awesome art talents – revealed!

Super Sculptor!

You're very intelligent, but you're also patient and kind. You have a keen interest in how things work... And that's why you'd make an amazing sculptor!

✓ Check out Trafalgar Square in London for amazing monuments and sculptures!

Jazzy Jeweller!

You love everything to be bright, bold and beautiful! You're popular and chatty and love everything clothes-related. Why not try being a jewellery designer?

✓ Check out Cartier — the world's most famous jewellers!

Amazing Illustrator!

You and your bezzies are an artistic bunch and you like to show them your creations. We think life as an illustrator would suit you best!

✓ Check out Nick Sharratt's top drawing tips on page 74!

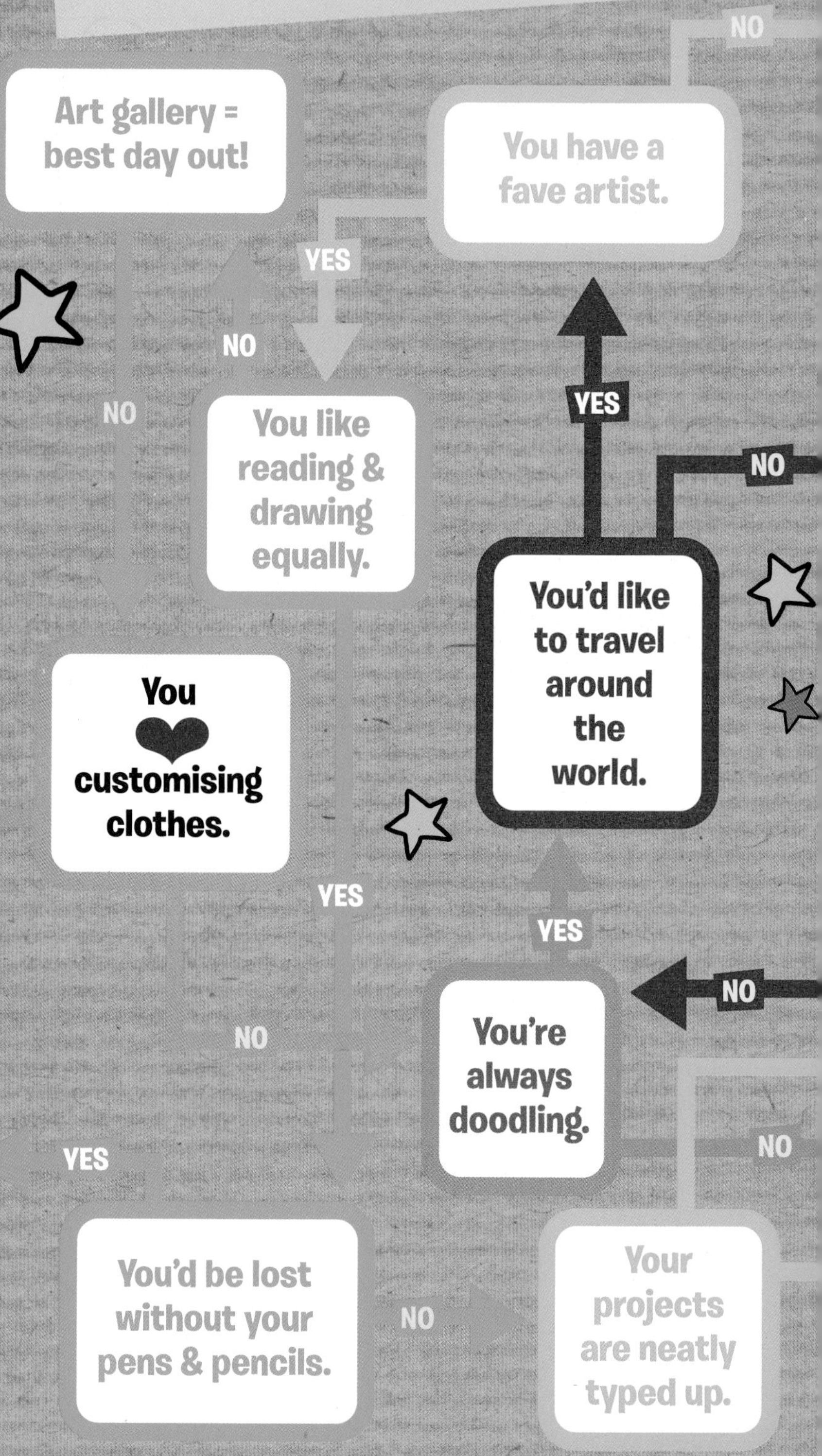

Should You Be?

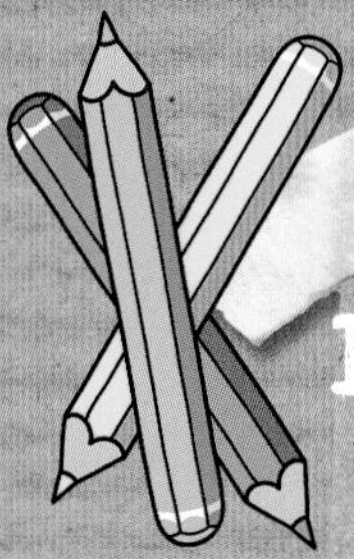

START here and follow the arrows

You're always online. — YES → You prefer an e-reader to books. / NO → You're always looking for the latest apps.

You're always looking for the latest apps. — YES → You help your parents on the computer. / NO → You make new friends easily.

You prefer an e-reader to books. — YES → You help your parents on the computer. / NO → Great Graphic Designer!

You help your parents on the computer. — YES → Wonderful Web Designer! / NO → You like to show off your creations.

You make new friends easily. — YES → A photo frame = my perfect prezzie! / NO → You like to show off your creations.

You've got sooo many photo albums! — YES → A photo frame = my perfect prezzie! / NO → You make new friends easily.

A photo frame = my perfect prezzie! — YES → Fantastic Photographer! / NO → You like to show off your creations.

You like to show off your creations. — YES → Great Graphic Designer! / NO → Fantastic Photographer!

Fantastic Photographer!

You're friendly, enthusiastic and always see the best in people — that's why you're destined to be a photographer!

✓ Check out your family's old albums for posing tips

Great Graphic Designer!

Quirky, creative and not afraid to try new things — that's totally you! Why not try your hand at some graphic design?

✓ Check out Blaine — our graphic designer's work — right here!

Wonderful Web Designer!

Everyone turns to you when they have a technological problem, but you're also brilliantly imaginative. We think you'd make it as a web designer one day!

✓ Check out www.jw-mag.com for inspiration!

Mighty Mart Vs The Pongy Pink Lady!

Marty loves drawing comic strips featuring her superhero self, Mighty Mart. Can you fill in the speech and thought bubbles to finish her latest story?

Nick's Tip!

- Look at the pictures and try to think about what could be happening in each one.
- Keep your speech to the point — it'll help your comic flow better!

ZAP!
POW!

King For A Day!

What would Nick do if he ruled the country?

If I was king for the day...

I'd have smoked salmon and scrambled eggs for breakfast, pasta with fresh pesto sauce for lunch and fish and chips for dinner.

My crown would be knitted so it would be nice and soft against my bald head.

I'd ride around on a bicycle — it's my favourite mode of transport.

My palace would be built like a Scottish castle.

My royal motto would be "An apple a day".

I'd ban trousers that hang so low they show your underpants.

I'd pass a law making it illegal to talk on a mobile phone at the same time as paying a shop assistant. How rude is that?

My national anthem would be *We Are Family*, a funky disco tune from the 1970s.

I'd give a knighthood to Jamie Oliver for his efforts to improve school dinners.

I'd make Jacqueline Wilson a dame — that's handy, she already is!

Cut & Create!
Use these with your games and makes.
Fun stuff to cut, colour and stick!

Bunny Bag Charm

Template

Trace this pattern and cut two of everything to make your bunny charm.

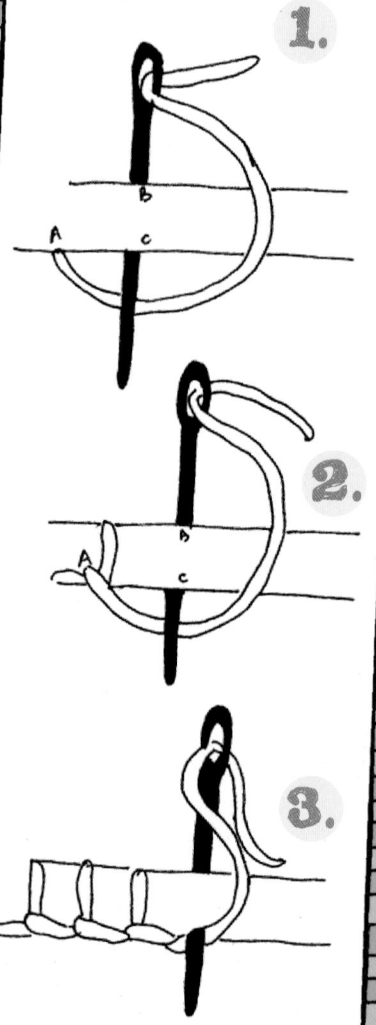

Blanket Stitching

Make a knot at the end of your piece of thread and start a tiny stitch at point A as shown. Put your needle in 1cm from the edge of the fabric, put the thread under the point of the needle and then pull the needle with the rest of the thread through. Repeat until finished.

STORY SPINNER

For the Happy Ending Game on page 22.

- Stick the top half of the page to card and cut out the spinner and arrow. Loosely attach the arrow to the spinner with a paper fastener.
- Spin and match the number with the story starters on page 22. Now you just have to write a happy ending to the sad tale!

CUT 'N' STICK SHAPES

Make Your Destiny Decider!

Use this to play the cliff hanger game on page 24.

What to do!
- Pick a number between 1 and 4.
- Open and close the square the same number of times.
- Pick a JW character.
- Open and close again as you spell out their name.
- Pick another character and look under the flap to find your story idea.

MAKE IT!

1. Cut out the Destiny Decider and turn it over so this side is face down.

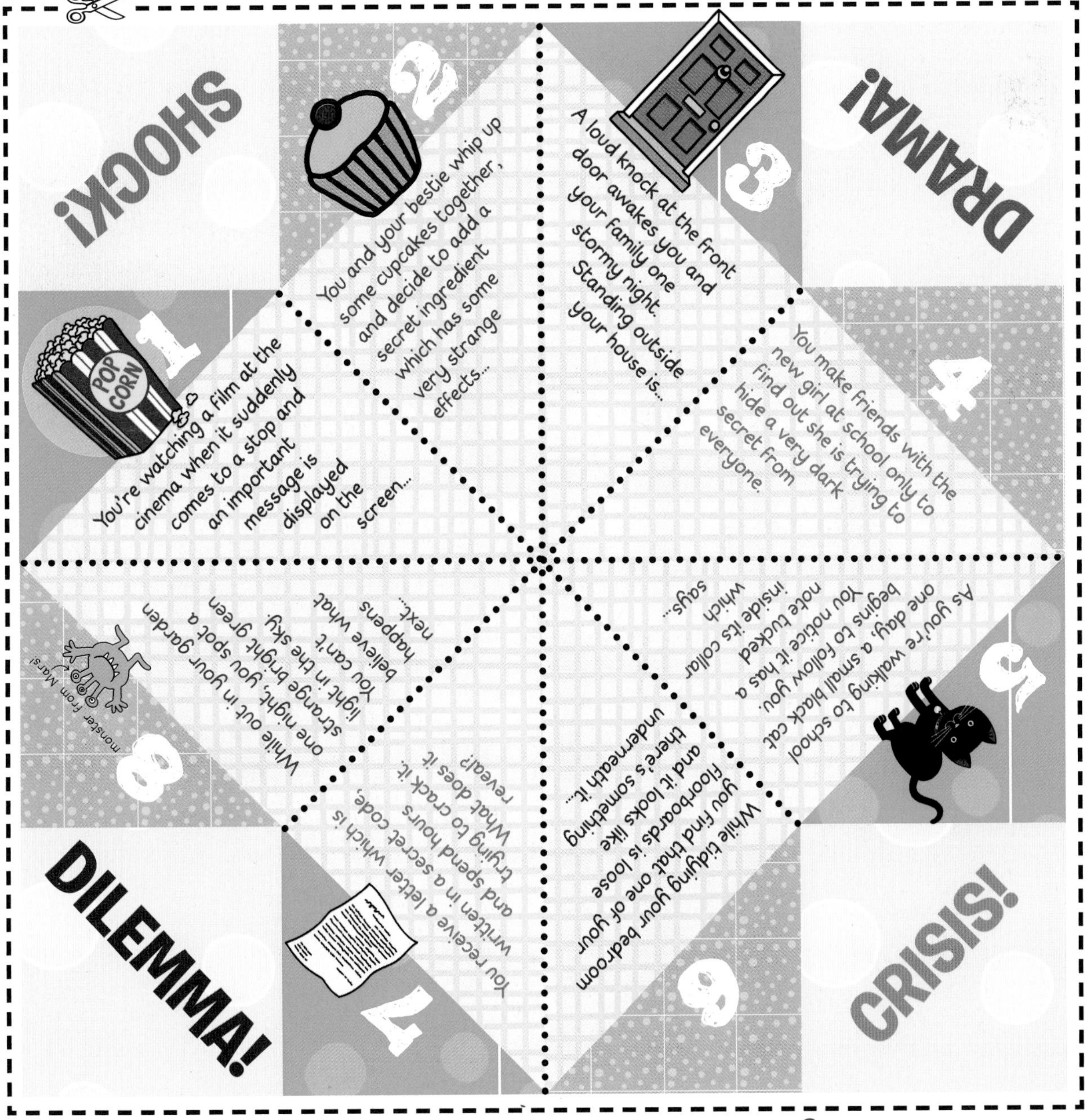

2. Fold each corner into the centre to make a diamond shape.

3. Flip it over and fold the corner into the middle again.

4. Fold the square in half.

5. Put your thumbs and forefingers under each flap and push the four corners together to meet in the middle.

Cut & Create!

Decorate your notebooks with these snip 'n' stick pictures

Triple Gold Star

I ♥ Books

Totally cool

Beaker-tastic

Super-cool

Tremendous

I ♥ JW

I'm the greatest!

poster paints
The Official
Jacqueline Wilson
Mag
sweeties
yum!